of philosophy returns

The Masquerader unmasked

ERIE

NORTH HAVEN ISLAND

LAWRENCE •

A city full of Ghosts

Demara is Kidnapped

The first perfect Dry Martini ever made in Glinty Glo

He goes into the night— But who is he?

Trapped by the Trappists

GETHSEMANI

The Birds fly away with the Notebook

NASHVILLE

The Death Wagon dies here

MISSISSIPPI

He makes a Speech for Integration Here

GET NEXT TO GOD
Revival Tonight

The Impostor saves 300 souls

THE RASCAL
AND THE ROAD

Also by Robert Crichton
The Great Impostor

ROBERT CRICHTON

The Rascal and the Road

Random House  *New York*

For My Father

He despaired of the project from the start. He was convinced the journey out on the road was inspired by idiocy and tainted with some madness. But it was Kyle who, when the whole project was on the tilting edge of disaster, salvaged it all by his real encouragement and his real money, neither of which he was ever prone to squander.

NOTE TO READER

In the last 18 years Ferdinand W. ("Fred") Demara has assumed the names, characters and careers of more men than he can recall. Some of his most startling impostures are listed in Robert Crichton's book, THE GREAT IMPOSTOR, published by Random House:

Science Instructor at a boys' school in Arkansas.

Catholic Brother at Trappist and other monasteries in 10 states and Canada.

Naval Surgeon who performed many operations as an officer in the Canadian Navy during the war in Korea.

Latin Master at the North Haven, Maine, high school.

College Dean, School of Philosophy, Gannon College, Pennsylvania.

Deputy Warden at the Huntsville state penitentiary, the maximum security lockup of the Texas prison system.

College Founder who helped get Notre Dame Normal School, a junior college in Maine, accredited as a four-year institution.

Cancer Researcher with the Brothers of Christian Instruction, a Catholic order.

Auditor at the Lamar Hotel in Houston, Texas.

Teacher of Eskimos at a school in Point Barrow, Alaska.

1.

The entanglement of myself with the impostor Demara, an alliance so ridden with rareness that it never ceases to startle me when I look back on it, could only have happened on the day it did, and even the very hour.

I knew from the moment I opened my eyes that morning that something vexatious, something way out of line, was going to happen. I knew it when I watched my wife Judy come in from the landing reading the morning newspaper.

"I see they've caught that Ferdinand Waldo Demara again," she said.

I didn't recognize it then, but that was the beginning of the whole unholy alliance.

"And just who is Waldo Demara?" I asked.

The moment of genesis. As direct and decisive as the birth of a baby, there is no going back or putting back. The start is begun. How many times I have regretted ever asking that question; and then how many times I have been glad that I did.

So that was the start but I can see one other thing now. If it hadn't been for the party we held the night before, none of what happened after that question ever would have happened.

We had held a St. Valentine's Day party for the children the afternoon before, and when their guests had gone away, taking their baskets of heart-shaped candies and scarlet balloons with them, my wife decided that we should hold a spontaneous Festival of Love on St. Valentine's night to reaffirm love in a loveless world. It must be a good idea to hold a party unabashedly dedicated to love since everyone came and it was a great party. I can say that without boasting because this is a chronicle, a record of things past, and I have a duty to tell things as they were.

People began by being nice to each other and then there was singing and dancing and all the while people were drinking deeply and well in a manner Hemingway would have approved so that by two o'clock in the morning, when the first guests went singing and shouting down into the cold, quiet streets, love had been reaffirmed on Perry Street. Even the police, when they came, felt the aura of it. They were very gentle.

I had gone to bed suffused in a glow of good fellowship for the world and everyone in it, and when I woke in the morning, much too early, the glow remained. The world seemed to be lit by a light of stunning purity flooding through the core of a crystal prism. Things that should have annoyed me, pleased me. Threading my way through the shambles of the living room I merely marveled at the guests' ingenuity in balancing drinks in implausible places.

"How weary, stale, flat and unprofitable seem to me all

the undrunk highballs of this world," I said aloud, and it seemed to me to be one of the wittiest things I ever heard—and profound.

The patterns of things were all in their right places. The world was a palace of promise filled with infinite possibilities. I felt ready to take on any challenge it could offer me. Had I been a practitioner of Yoga I would have suspected I was on the brink of experiencing a major mystical experience.

I didn't realize then that I was deep in the grip of that rarest of phenomenoms, a benevolent hangover. Ripeness is all. For a second time I said: "And just who is Waldo Demara?"

Judy began reading the news story of the impostor's latest "caper." This time he had been unmasked while masquerading as a Latin master at a high school in Maine. As she read I began to see the man clearly, since visions came easily that morning, trudging down out of the snowy fastness of Maine, in despair but not in disgrace, exiled to his home in Lawrence, Massachusetts.

"This man is a martyr," I cried out, with great emotion. I told Judy how I could see him as one of the last true American individualists, standing alone against the tyranny of conformity, defying bureaucratic pomposity and making a mockery of the organization man. I impressed Judy; I was inspired and it was catching. She in turn saw this Demara as The Great Actor, a man who every moment of his desperate life was acting and playing a role to the hilt, but an actor who also had to create his own characters and play all of his own parts and supply all his own lines.

"And they have to be perfect lines," Judy said. "He can never write a false one."

"He can't even blow one," I said.

It was a staggering, exhilarating thought. I went over to the mirror in the living room, that was still festooned with purple and red streamers which had cascaded down the walls of the room, and tried to imagine myself in the role of the great impostor. I saw him, even felt him, facing himself in the mirror in the morning, preparing the script for the day, creating and killing lines, thinking swiftly, even savagely, mouthing and polishing the phrases he would have to spring on the stage of his world that day.

"Do you know what this man needs?" I said. "He needs a writer."

After a moment's thought we both knew that was impossible. The impostor must remain anonymous or the masquerade would be over, but then Judy declared passionately that this man deserved at least a biographer to write the stories of all his lives before something fatal happened, and they were forever lost.

I went into the kitchen to get several bowls of corn flakes I had been promising the children, and when I came out I saw a look on my wife's face that made me think that she had just been host to a profound visitation.

"Ferdinand Waldo Demara has a writer," she said.

"He does?" I asked. "Who?"

"You."

On any other day that idea would have died long before it ever learned to crawl. But I was wrapped in my optimistic glow. I wore it around with me like a kimono and I felt as secure as a silkworm in a cocoon. I tried to think of reasons why I shouldn't be the famed impostor's biographer.

"I'm just not the man for it," I argued. "He'll want someone famous, a big reputation."

"Wrong," Judy said. "*He* wants to be the somebody. What he wants is a good, competent cipher."

It made sense, as did all the other things she said. The patterns of things were all in their right places. I finally agreed to approach the impostor if Mr. Jerry Norton agreed that it was a sound project. Mr. Norton had been a part-time father to my wife, a former editor, literary agent and publisher, and a man considered to possess a keen sense of values as far as literary "properties" were concerned. From across the room I could hear him talking to Judy.

It was Mr. Norton's opinion that we had latched onto "a genuine American literary stinkbomb." The heart of his argument was that Demara was a "no-like guy" like Pretty Boy Floyd and that if I wanted to write books for the edification of "hoodlums and creeps" that I should go right ahead. But his suggestion was that we should flee from the project as if it were a ticking bomb. She hung up the phone and turned to me.

"Jerry's not *too* keen on it," she said. "He feels the character lacks a certain nobility."

That certainly should have ended the adventure right then, but I made no protest when Judy phoned Dan Melnick, a member of her family who had vowed to become a television network vice-president before he was thirty and who had succeeded with several years to spare. I thought of him as a kind of human nerve center, a restless radar screen scanning the city, recording every blip of significant action. Melnick was more positive; he felt the idea was born and conceived in greatness, like the Republic, and said that he would sue for criminal negligence if the "package" wasn't tied up within the hour.

"Who's going to pen the thing?" he asked, and when Judy told him, there was a thin, cool hiss of air, as if he had just been pierced by a small dart. But he recovered well.

"Ah, well, the editors can always tack it together in case everything goes wrong," he said. I had been listening on the extension and far from being hurt, I felt this was sage advice.

"Tell Bob for me," Melnick summed up, "he'd be stupid if he didn't do it."

When I came back into the room I asked Judy what Dan had said.

"He said, Tell Bob for me, he'd be smart if he did it."

So I had earned my commission to go ahead. Much later I realized that we would have telephoned all morning until we had found a Dan Melnick. Ordinarily the idea of telephoning long distance worries me and telephoning a stranger long distance can often ruin an entire day, but this morning I marched to the phone and asked the operator for Lawrence, Massachusetts. After a confused wait I was finally told that Mr. Demara's line was out of order, and just before I hung up the operator confided in me.

"It's not exactly out of order," she said. "He tore the thing out of the wall and threw it out of the window."

And that should have been the end of the affair, but I thought of Farwell Potter who lives in Andover, the next town to Lawrence, and I called him. Old Farwell said he would be delighted to zip over to Lawrence and "take the bull-thrower by the horns."

"I'll beard the liar in his den. After all," Farwell said, "It takes a Tartar to catch a Tartar."

Potter is from Boston and he tries very hard to live the adventurous life. Although he is a genuine war hero, he never quite has been able to establish himself as a regular fellow; he is a sort of Mickey Spillane corrupted by a Groton education.

We waited all day for Farwell to report back and as I waited a serious thing began to happen. The great good glow began to fade and the old, real me began to re-emerge. By the time he did call I had reached a stage of terror about what I had gotten myself into. My fear was that Farwell would succeed.

The lawn of the Demara home, he reported, was being trampled into a quagmire by a round-the-clock mob of reporters, wire-service people, television representatives, publishers' representatives, agents, free-lance writers and operators, all waiting to put some proposition to Demara. Despite all the things he had done before, Demara suddenly, as a personality, was a "hot property." But he was not cooperating, and he even threatened one person with a piece of textile machinery he had in his house as a door stop. One man momentarily got his attention, Farwell said, by appearing out on the lawn with six children.

"If I don't get an interview," he called up, "I lose my job, and these children will starve."

For a moment the strategy seemed to work. The children were "pitiful tads" in Potter's words, but then the impostor hardened and announced it would at least be the first positive step in halting the population explosion.

Although he wasn't there when it happened, Potter reported that a group of Harvard psychology students had come up from Cambridge and camped on the grass. They wanted the impostor to submit to a crash-program battery of psychological testings.

"You owe it to the world," a student pleaded.

"Go away, you fakes," Demara roared. "I used to *teach* your subject."

After that Farwell described his unsuccessful efforts to gain an interview, and as he did I felt my whole system responding joyously.

"You tried your best, Farwell, you did all a man could do," I said, but he was disconsolate.

"I guess I'm not much of a Tartar after all," he said, and hung up.

I tried to disguise my joy from Judy. The sun had gone down and I felt it would be proper to mix a drink. I made a martini and sat before our little grate and watched a chunk of cannel coal stutter and flutter with smoke and light, and thought how fortunate I was. The children were playing happily in the next room, outside the deep velvety sweetness of a cold winter night was settling in, turning the snow on the window sill a deep, rich, cold blue and I wasn't going to have to probe into the secret lives of some man I didn't know and who I had grown afraid of.

"Well, that's it. The ledger shut, the account closed, chapter and book ended. I've tried everything I could."

"You could always write him a letter," Judy said.

It was a simple thing, an old-fashioned technique not many people seem to think of any more. The idea annoyed me because I couldn't be at ease with myself until I had tried every door. I put down my drink, got out my typewriter and wrote a letter. It was not a good letter, and I had the double satisfaction of knowing I had written a letter he wouldn't reply to and yet feeling I had done my duty to the end.

As I knew would happen, we didn't hear from him after that. Days stretched into weeks and soon we no longer mentioned the impostor and finally ceased to think of him. I do a lot of business with Boston and so it was with no anticipation of any kind that I opened the plain, rather grimy envelope postmarked from that city. Inside there was a single sheet of tablet-type writing paper. The letter was written in ink with a bold, clear, firm hand. The message on it is a masterpiece of artistic economy and showed a mind that had a reverence for not wasting words. This is it in full:

> I like a writer who *writes.*
> You look like the man.
> > *Demara*

2.

I took the note as a summons to greatness.

"He wants me," I shouted up the stairwell, and when Judy came out onto the landing and looked down at me waving the piece of paper, she knew immediately what I meant.

I went into action at once. I telephoned two magazine editors and canceled several article assignments I had worked hard to get. I am afraid that in my elation I was rather high-handed about doing it, using a kind of fare-well-to-Grub-Street attitude that did not endear me to them. I went to the library and scanned the old newspaper files, ordered back papers, called everyone for advice on what to do with a great defrauder. Only my father had not been impressed by the note when I read it to him.

"You look like the man to do what?" he asked me.

Of course I had no answer and felt none was needed, but as the days began to lengthen into weeks that unanswered question loomed bigger and bigger. I finally had to swallow my pride after the second quiet week and beg to be allowed to rejoin the ranks on Grub Street and begin to plan ahead for a life without the impostor in it.

We had grown accustomed to it, even liking it, when the telephone rang at exactly six o'clock one morning.

"Be at Delfondo's at exactly one o'clock for lunch," the voice at the other end said. The voice had been deep and controlled. It had also been ominous.

"Who was it?" Judy asked me, but I knew she knew.

"Him," I said. We didn't say anything for a fairly long time and finally Judy said that she didn't like it, that it frightened her in fact.

"Bob, he *ordered* you," she said. I tried to deny that he had ordered me but finally admitted that he had.

"We've made a mistake," Judy said, "and it's as much my fault as yours. We've gotten into something people like us aren't prepared to handle. Make me a promise. Promise me that you won't go to that restaurant."

I finally persuaded my wife that the least I owed the man was to meet him for lunch if he had come down from New England to see me.

"After all," I said, "he can't exactly do something to me in a restaurant in New York at high noon."

"I don't know why not, he's done things more outlandish than that."

It was true, I thought with some nervousness, as I was on my way uptown for lunch. In the weeks of waiting I had felt the legend of the impostor grow so large that by now Demara assumed superman proportions in my imagination. I was going to go, but I wasn't surprised to find that my legs were trembling.

I arrived a half-hour early to be certain to be on time and waited. Delfondo's is a large, run-down rococco wreck of a place favored by bit actors and horse players who do not have the money to afford a good Jewish delicatessen but who need a place to wait for calls and study form sheets. I wondered why he had chosen the place. I also wondered how he was going to identify me.

I stayed until three o'clock in the afternoon and then I left. I found it hard to admit to Judy I had waited that long to no avail when I went home.

"Well, that ends it," Judy said. "You have met your obligation and that ends it."

I felt, as Judy did, that he was toying with me, playing a kind of sadistic game of cat and mouse, and yet I couldn't be sure. There was always the chance that something legitimate had happened to delay the man. In this man's strange, illegitimate world many factors must be operating when he makes a date.

He telephoned at six o'clock the next morning.

"I'm disappointed in you but I'm giving you a second chance," the voice said. "Be in Grafello's at noon and take the table near the service door."

"I forbid you to go near that place," Judy said. "Promise me that."

Rather then tell her of my own doubts I made the promise and I broke it. At eleven thirty I began walking slowly across the West Side of New York and a few minutes before noon, to lessen the waiting time, I entered Grafello's.

I had no hopes for the day. I waited an hour and

then felt I should wait one more. In boredom I studied one of the trees nearby me. They were ebony, a dusty ebony, and were fashioned in the kind of design popular in the mid-1920's, and sometimes characterized as "modren." I was wondering why such an old-fashioned, run-down place as Grafello's had ever invested in them, with all the other things that so badly needed repairing, when I realized with a certain little horror that the trees were alive. The ebony color was merely the accumulated grime of generations. I spent my third hour, with the head waiter's reluctant permission, washing the leaves until they glowed a fresh green, green-gold with life, and the whole performance gave me a little heart to endure.

On the morning of the third day the phone rang again at its accustomed time. I had planned to answer with some scathing insult, but Demara's voice at the other end seized the initiative.

"You were *marvelous,*" the voice boomed. "You were great. You showed me all I needed to know about you."

I didn't know what to say, and I remained silent.

"You showed me endurance, you showed me patience, you showed me loyalty. All those things I demand. And," the impostor added ominously, "let me say this: You're going to need them."

"What makes you so sure *I* want to do this?" I finally asked.

"Because you are a writer. And I have a fascinating story to write."

I am always stopped by the truth and this was, of course, the truth. I then asked him how he even knew I was a writer.

"Anyone who can sit in one of those places for three and four hours and do nothing—he's *got* to be a writer. The non-creative mind," he explained, "would go mad."

"But why those places?" I asked. His voice sounded suddenly a little distant, a little disappointed, even a little hurt.

"You, my biographer. The great impostor's biographer has to ask a question like that?"

I tried as hard as possible and could think of no plausible reason.

"Big Brother was *watching* you."

I was stunned by the news and tried to think of all the things I had done while he studied me. How foolish I must have looked.

"I like what you did with that tree," he said. "That was creative."

But even with his explanation of watching me, I still didn't see why it had to be those places, those weary, over-decorated, turn-of-the-century funeral parlors.

"You don't really know?" he asked in disgust, and I had to admit it. With a fine feeling for theatrics, he said no more until I was driven to ask him *why* again.

"Potted palms to peer from," he said, and hung up.

3.

I did not hear from Ferdinand Demara again for several days. For the second time, I dropped the magazine assignments I had been working on, to my professional near ruin, and went back to immersing myself in the lives of Demara. The phone rang, however, early one evening and Demara announced that it was now time to get on with our work.

The impostor is impressive, even commanding on the phone. No matter how much inner assurance I felt at the time of a call, it would all melt away before I could open my mouth. He asked me where we should meet and, as was usual, I found I had no idea. When I failed to answer he suggested that we meet at eleven o'clock on Thursday in the garden of the United Nations.

"It will be neutral ground. Don't bother to bring a lawyer or agent; I don't trust them," he said. "We'll be on international territory, anyway, so that anything we say to each other won't be binding."

I told him that I thought it was a wonderful idea, even a brilliant one, and then I proceeded to ask him how I would recognize him.

"Don't you remember," he said, in a cold voice that chilled me.

I had disappointed him again. "I will recognize *you*."

He had established a manner of making me feel perpetually off-balance. I could feel my foot slipping into my mouth, with growing regularity.

For the next two days I was actually sick and this infuriated Judy.

"You're acting like a spoiled, neurotic, high school kid," she admonished me. "He's only a man."

"And that's just where you're wrong," I insisted.

"He's not just a man, he's all sorts of men, all kinds that I could never be."

But beneath it all was the fear that perhaps I was to be the latest victim in some kind of plot this man had hatched. I had already established a respect for his mind but how could I be certain of his morality? He *posed* as the good impostor—an intellectual Robin Hood who did bad only to do eventual good; that I knew all about. But suppose there were times when there hadn't been good; only bad. Suppose there were people who were no longer in any position to talk about those times, people whose mouths, which might tell a different story, were forever shut?

There was also the natural fear of my own failure and then there was the simple peasant's fear of being gulled, conned and cozened by one of the master gullers of all time. I made a vow to myself that I would sign nothing and agree to nothing.

On the morning of the day, strangely, my sickness, or weakness, whichever it was, had vanished. Now that I knew I must at last face my adversary a fatalistic calm overtook me. For the first time that week I was able to eat a plate of eggs and bacon. I even felt chipper as I took the bus up to 42nd Street to catch the crosstown bus to the United Nations.

When I got off the bus I rediscovered that it was cold and felt that was the reason my legs began trembling again. Tightly spun little clouds, hard, cold, rocky ones, were scudding over the Hell Gate Bridge to the north, driving down the East River from the Bronx and beyond, which added to the chill I felt within me. The clouds looked like small headstones on the move. When I entered the cold, formal, impersonal gardens, it was all I could do to keep my feet moving.

He was not in the park.

"I will give you five minutes," I said aloud to buoy up my sinking spirits. "You've got five to show."

After that five I planned to run. When I did I was not going to answer any phone for a week and, in fact, I was going to leave New York. I studied the second hand on my watch, studying it ticking away, each second gone freeing me from a liaison I had come to dread. I felt if I watched that second hand as hard as I could watch anything that I could force it along by my stare. I stared so hard and unblinkingly that the wind whipped little tears out of my eyes and finally I could no longer see the hands move or hear the watch ticking.

I felt his hand hit the small of my back and I very nearly leaped in the air and shouted out loud.

"And you will be Crichton," he said.

Because of the tears in my eyes, and since the sun was

behind him, I couldn't see him. My mouth had framed
the word "yes" but only a sound, perilously close to a
shriek, had come out. His voice came at me, disembodied,
as if coming from the depths of a wind tunnel. I again had
the urge to run.

"It's pronounced Cry-ton, is that correct?"

"Yes. Yes, it is," I said. "Amazing! Almost everyone gets
it wrong the first time."

"But then I'm not everyone. Am I?"

He had put out his hand for me to take and I hadn't
seen it. I noticed it just as he withdrew it and I thrust
mine out. Just as he went to seize it I withdrew it
again and in the process we both executed a kind of
courtly, clumsy little dance.

"Men of infinite poise," Demara said acidly. "There is
one thing I detest in this world above all others, and
that's being made to look ridiculous."

When I could see again my eyes went first to his feet to
see how he had managed to come up behind me on that
crunchy gravel without my hearing him. For a man his
size his feet were small, even dainty, but he wore standard
shoes; there was nothing unnatural about them.

He wore a big, blue, kapok-stuffed, fur-collared coat and
his hat was a regulation knitted United States Navy cap.
Somehow he managed to make the combination look
imperious and even a little lordly. He was taller than
his pictures had led me to believe and much heavier,
weighing then, I later learned, about 275 pounds. For a
person a little over six feet, it was far too much, but he
carried it well and, unlike many fat people, there was a
decided feeling of vitality and power about him, an ani-

mal vigor such as I have seen in some overweight professional football players.

What surprised me most were his eyes. His skin is olive, although ruddily olive, like the skin of French peasants who work out of doors, and his hair, always worn in a brush cut, is a rich, shiny dark brown, the kind of hair that belongs to people with dark brown eyes. But Demara's eyes are a bright, clear, nearly icy blue. They look like they belong to someone else. When he caught me staring at them, I dropped my own eyes.

"Oh, that's a good sign," he said. "It means you're basically an honest man. Only a dishonest man can stare you in the eyes for long. How did someone put it? 'Dishonesty will stare honesty out of countenance any day.' "

He told me other things then; that the truth is so complicated that the teller of truth can rarely wear the assured, confident look we expect of him. Only a crook or liar can assume that face for long. I wanted to write it all down, but he eyed my pencil.

"Don't bother with that. It annoys me," he said. "I have a thousand more like that."

We began walking along the gravel path leading out of the park, and while I didn't want to be forward I felt I should mention what we had come about.

"Oh, yes, business." He stopped and reflected for a moment or two, eyeing me keenly while I shifted back and forth from foot to foot, and then he thrust his hand out to me.

"Here's your contract," he said. "My hand is my bond. Fifty-fifty all the way down the line."

I had been warned not to agree to *anything*, but I knew

I couldn't resist that hand. I had no desire to. To resist the hand, in any event, meant to put an end to our project.

"No agents, no lawyers, no commission men, no ten-percenters, no papers, no contracts, no outsiders. All of them are parasites. One gentleman to another gentleman." He shook my hand again.

"My word, my bond. My hand, my seal. My witness"— he put his hand over his heart—"my God."

He looked around at the United Nations buildings that towered beyond us. "It's too bad the world can't operate this way. You know why they can't?"

I said that I didn't.

"Because most of the people in this world were never treated right. As such, they don't know how to treat others right. They have no manners. Manners are really a great luxury. The angel of peace will come disguised as Mr. Manners. Take that one down," he said.

We went across the street and had a cup of coffee out of the cold wind. Steam had clouded over the window of the small shop and it was warm and snug in there and I felt comfortable with the famed impostor. We relaxed and smoked and said nothing for a long time.

"I think it's been a profitable morning," Demara finally said. "I think that I can learn to like you."

I felt immensely flattered.

With his hand he made a circle in the fogginess of the window and through it looked out onto the street and the United Nations beyond.

"It's a propitious time to begin a project. How did Browning put it?"

I didn't know whether he expected me, his biographer, to begin quoting something or not. I didn't know which way to jump.

> *"The year's at the spring*
> *The day's at the morn;"*

"God's in his heaven," I added. He seemed pleased at that and motioned for me to join in.

"All's right with the world," we said together. He gave me a joyous smile.

And it was, too.

Then.

I was so excited about our prospects together that, although Demara might possibly hear me, I telephoned Judy.

"You call Mr. Norton for me," I ordered, "and you tell him that he is wrong, wrong, wrong. This is a much-like guy."

4.

We drew up a plan of battle. It was decided that before we considered any other refinements, the first thing we had to do was to produce a straight, coherent account of Demara's many and complex lives. At that time he couldn't even remember one or two of them. Once the whole mixed bag of histories was sorted out we could begin thinking about just how it might be told.

But this would call for money to live on and for a place to work. At the moment I had neither, but Random House agreed to put up an advance against future royalties once we signed a contract, and then a friend of mine, Don Nestingen, went off to South America to film a documentary movie, leaving his hotel apartment at our disposal. We planned to work there in the day and Demara could use it as home at night.

It was interesting that Demara, while excellent at names, was never able to get Nestingen's name right. Later I found out why. The impostor has an almost psychotic aversion to accepting charity. Even using an empty apartment compelled him to humble the donor by distorting his name. In this way Demara felt the balance between giver and taker evened and he was able to retain his independence.

On the morning that we were to go to Random House to sign the book contract Demara seemed highly uneasy. We met for breakfast at a cafeteria, and he wanted to know what Bennett Cerf, the publisher, was like. I told him that I thought he was very much as he appeared on television; I knew that Demara had seen Cerf many times. He was very annoyed at that.

"Don't give me that," he said angrily. "That's his public image. Don't you know even the most basic rules of behavior?"

He later explained to me what he had meant. To Demara any public image is always false, for it is necessary in public to present a controllable image and only a false image is controllable.

"Remember this, and don't forget it," he told me. "There is nothing more vulnerable and more unreliable than the truth."

I was to hear this belief repeated many times afterwards in various shapes. When you lie, Demara has learned, you can shape your material so that it has order and sense and meaning, so that it has the real semblance of truth. "When you have the truth, you have chaos," is one maxim. "As long as it seems like the truth, it works like the truth; and, thus, it becomes the truth," is another.

At times I found my head swimming with maxims I couldn't quite absorb or which I didn't want to believe and couldn't refute. Before going to Random House he insisted that we stop off at "Nestinghen's"—that was his current way of saying it—to get a fresh shirt.

It was a revelation to enter the room.

Although Demara had been there only a day or two he had settled in nicely. It was clear that when he had the chance to do it, he liked to live one way, which was high. While he was changing his shirt I surveyed the room. There were bottles of imported Holland beer neatly stacked about and there was a small, inexpensive wine rack which held nearly a dozen bottles of good red and white French wines. When I looked into the kitchenette and refrigerator I knew I was in the company of a gourmet. There was a comprehensive collection of imported delicatessen tidbits and delicacies that can run high. It was apparent to me that, guessing on the size of the advance that awaited us at Random House, we might soon founder by the cost of the impostor's snacks alone.

"You've made yourself right at home," I said. He came out of the room and stared at me.

"Why don't you say what you mean?" he said. "I don't believe in *stinting,* if that's what you mean."

I found myself reddening and had to turn away to hide it.

Although we were in easy walking distance to the publisher Demara insisted we take a taxi and then, when we were halfway there, he announced that he couldn't go the way he was.

"You can go the way *you* are," he said, eyeing my sports jacket and flannels with a certain distaste. "You're an artist. At least a pseudo-artist," he gratuitously offered. "But I am a personality. I arrive in a taxi. I arrive well dressed for the occasion."

I was surprised by this display of common bourgeois

manners. Only later did I find that this need to conform to standards is, oddly enough, one of the things that drives Demara into the implausible escapades that make up his life.

I did a silly thing. I told him that it didn't really matter what he wore because we probably wouldn't see Bennett Cerf in the first place.

"*I* see Bennett Cerf. I don't know about *you,*" he said to me in a voice both cold and trembling with barely controlled anger. "I go to the top. Here's another one to remember. Here's one I live by and it's one reason I've been so successful." He waited for just the correct moment.

"First stop! The *top!*"

"You're telling the truth, brother," the cab driver said, swinging around and eyeing Demara with admiration. "The rest of them are just there to say no."

"This is a guy who *understands,*" Demara said to me. "Say. Can you write?" he said to the driver. "I think I got a job for you."

It was meant to make me feel miserable, of course, and it did. I spent a wretched fifteen minutes breaking our appointment at Random House and guaranteeing that Mr. Cerf would see us. It turned out that he had no intention of missing the master faker. After the call we took another taxi and went downtown to Maxey's, a huge, low-overhead kind of place that guarantees to fit anyone, even a Demara, from their racks. When we reached the place Demara surprised me by asking me to wait on the sidewalk. He came out several minutes later and motioned for me to move across the avenue with him, where we took

a post opposite the front door of the store. For a moment
I had a horrible feeling that he was going to pull off some
kind of heist and that I was, like it or not, an accom-
plice. Shortly afterward, two sales people came out of the
door and started down Seventh Avenue, I suspect for
lunch, and Demara nudged me to follow him.

Inside the store he took another minute to size up the
personnel and then approached a young salesman from the
rear.

"Feldman," he said. "Chester Feldman?" the man
turned, somewhat startled. I could see from a celluloid
covered name plate that this was, indeed, his name.

"You don't know me, but you know about me," Demara assured him. The man didn't deny this.

"Mr. Ross out on the Island—*you* know Mr. Ross—Mr.
Ross asked Mr. Stirling to take care of me and Mr. Stirling
said in case he wasn't here he wanted his right-hand man,
Chester, to look after me."

"He did?" young Feldman said, openly flattered that
Mr. Stirling, clearly his boss, had noticed him and singled
him out in such a fashion.

From that point it was easy. Mr. Feldman ran off to
show Demara the suits he had; and when Demara chose
one, it was merely a matter of asking to send Feldman
battling his way into the tailors to get an immediate fitting and alterations. While the needles were flashing
Demara came into his element, joshing the tailors, flattering Mr. Feldman and charming everyone involved.

Outside I said: "That was Mr. Stirling we saw come
out of the store?"

"Of course," he said, giving me the look of an adult

tolerating a child's questions. At the risk of getting the look again I felt I had to ask him how he dared use Stirling's name that way and what would have happened had Stirling arrived back in the middle of his game.

"I would simply seize the initiative. I was looking for him. I would rush up to him and say, 'Mr. Stirling, wonderful to see you. Mr. Ross, out on the Island, sends you his very best. He's on his way to Europe again you know.' What can Stirling think? He'll think he met the man at some lodge meeting or something and he'll think he's rich. Feldman's in no position to say a word; he'll just bask in the glory of being of impeccable service."

I noted that it was a nice piece of human handling and thought this would please him but he turned on me.

"Don't give me any of those holier-than-thou Presbyterian looks," he said. "Did I hurt anyone? I did like hell. I made them feel good."

I didn't know what to think. My morality seemed to be becoming increasingly like that wash-day tragedy. Once everything was black and white and now everything seemed to be coming up tattle-tale gray.

When we started up the stairs at Random House, Demara was in high spirits. He was resplendent in his new suit and one could sense that people were observing him closely. We were introduced to Donald Klopfer, the firm's vice-president and then to Mr. Cerf. It was all very urbane and the paneled wood of the offices pleased Demara's sense of occasion and dignity. He is a big believer in the proper form and style, which is rather strange in a man who breaks all the other proprieties.

After the ease of our United Nations agreement, however, I was astonished to see the interest Demara took in the contract.

"When I was director of publications at St. Martin's" (a college he had taught at in Washington), "we'd never agree to a restrictive clause like this one," he said at one point.

I went off to see another editor about certain things, leaving the negotiations to Demara, and when I came back someone said that he felt that he had been attending the Versailles Conference, there being so much inking out and initialing in. "And your impostor was playing Lloyd George," he said, "right up to the hilt."

It was late when the contract signing was done, but Demara and I were treated to a tour of the building. Random House is, literally, a house—an archaic, anachronistic, charming remnant of New York, standing implausibly proud and apart from the overbearing, ever-boring glass and brick of Madison Avenue.

"Charming but outmoded," Demara whispered to me. "Tear it down. The world has no place for sentiment."

Something bothered me as we left, some quickness of movement that didn't seem legitimate to me. It was nothing that I saw but more something that I felt.

When we went outside Demara proposed we have a drink at the New Weston bar across the way, and while we drank it he sensed that I had a feeling something was very wrong.

"Something's bothering you. Something's got you," he said. He was really taunting me but I didn't quite realize it. "What is it? You tell me."

I couldn't bring myself to mention what disturbed me.

After a second drink he opened the front of his new coat, smiled triumphantly, and produced a whole gallery of stationery, envelopes and memo pads, including personal stationery from Cerf and Klopfer. I was aghast.

"Now you take it easy, Crichton." It was the nearest he had come to being personal. I was still calling him Mr. Demara. "This stationery will never be used in any un-ethical way for any unethical purpose. I want you to be-lieve that right now, or I want you to have the courage to call this whole thing off."

I don't know whether I believed him or not. I wanted to. Perhaps I merely was afraid of calling off a project I already had devoted so much time and feeling to.

"I believe you," I said, and we shook hands. We had another drink and then talked with enthusiasm about our plans for beginning the interviewing the next day. He told me that I might call him Fred and I suggested he call me Bob, and then I felt I had better get going. Just as I was leaving he patted the pack of stationery.

"Of course, this just might get us out of a hell of a lot of trouble someday," he said, with a waggish grin.

I didn't pretend to know what he meant and I didn't want to know.

"Good night, Bob. Good night, partner," he said.

"Good night, Fred," I said, and it sounded a little odd to me.

Outside it was almost dark and the city was steeped in that soft, dark velvety light that only New York seems to get. The city surrounds itself with a hint of magic and even the simplest things take on a suspicion of romance; a light in a tenement window all at once looks warm and inviting and the urge to run home and get inside a room becomes overpowering. I felt sorry for the aloneness of Demara then, but I didn't feel I could bring him home yet.

On the sidewalk outside the New Weston, glued to the pavement in a little puddle of water, I saw a piece of Random House stationery from an editor's desk, and that posed a problem.

Was my responsibility to Random House to tell them Demara had taken some stationery, or was it to Demara to take his word that no harm would come from any of this? I decided to walk home and while I was walking I realized what I had to do.

I decided that I had to stop worrying about Demara's morality and concentrate on my own. I couldn't be a partner in crime; I'd only botch it anyway. If I found him doing something that was evil to society, as a member of it I had to try and stop him. But beyond that, I decided that I could leave Demara to God to worry about.

At home I was so excited about having resolved the moral dilemma that had been increasingly gnawing at me that I was in exuberant spirits.

"I think that Fred and I are going to make it," I said to Judy.

"Fred who?"

"Fred Demara," I said.

"My, you've come a long way."

I had, indeed. I could hardly wait for the next day to begin.

5.

The day began early enough. The telephone rang at seven o'clock.

"Don't bother to come up," Demara said. "I'm not going through with this. The contract, as of this moment, is null and void."

I was speechless. Watching me, Judy, for a brief second, felt I was having a stroke. All that my mind would allow me to think about right then was the Moslem custom of ending a marriage: "I divorce thee, I divorce thee, I divorce thee."

I was, unfortunately, already familiar with Demara's theory of contracts. It is his belief that any contract must benefit both parties equally. If, at any time, the balance shifts to one side, the other side has the moral right to declare the contract no longer operable. The terms are not being lived up to; the contract is null and void.

He told me where he felt the balance was shifting against him. The sum of his argument was that what I, and the public, wanted was the false Demara. He had been aghast at himself the day before, he said, acting the prima donna, spilling stolen stationery all over a public bar, conning the innocents of the world.

"That's not the real me. That's the me the world wants. I won't give it to you." I finally managed to ask him what we were going to do.

"I don't know what *we're* going to do. I am leaving now. I have left Nitrogen's in good shape and I want to thank you for everything. There's nothing personal here. I still think I could have gotten to like you."

Before I could think of any suitable answer he had hung up. I turned to Judy.

"He's leaving me," I said.

"My God," she said, with profound disgust, "you sound like his mistress."

It was true. I had to get over that. Every time I felt I had found the proper way to act with the impostor, it collapsed around me. Now everything had collapsed around me. By complete chance my car, which I almost never use in the city, was parked outside on Perry Street. I had been dressing while talking to Demara and now I ran down and got in the car and by an even greater chance the old engine started up at once. I got across town without hitting a light and up to the Beaux Arts Apartments in perhaps ten minutes in all. He was astonished when I appeared at the door. He thought I was the boy come for the bags.

"I don't want to talk about this," he said. "I-do-not-want-to-talk. Null means null, void is void, and end is end."

He closed the second of his two bags with a decisive smack. I suspect that I looked as defeated as I felt. I had no plans to try to persuade the impostor. The adventure had already cost me a great deal of time and a good deal of money that would never be redeemed, but there was something other than that which made me want to go on with it. I suppose it was challenge—the challenge of the job and also a certain challenge with myself.

"All right," he said, studying the length of my face, "I'll explain."

He told me how he had spent the entire previous night trying to think of a way to tell me his story. The words wouldn't come.

"I can't *talk* about those things, do you understand? I'm not proud of those things, can you see? I'm not ashamed of them, don't think that. But I'm not *proud* of them."

He went over to the window and pressed his head against the glass and looked down onto the East River below.

"All the people. All the good people I've fooled and cheated and taken advantage of. Do you think I can talk about that? Boast about it?"

I am not a persistent person. I think that only the strange, faraway look that filled his eyes as he stared unseeing out at the river prompted me to say anything.

"Did you ever think of going back?" I asked. "Seeing them for a last time? Back to the schools and colleges and monasteries. Back to Texas?" I didn't have any plan and I didn't mean anything by it.

For a while he said nothing and then he said: "Texas is very beautiful in the spring, at least the part I knew."

We talked for a time about some of the places I had lived and a lot of the places he had lived.

"Erie and the Great Lakes will still be deep in snow,"

he said wistfully. As we talked it began to occur to me, perhaps in a cunning way, that I could think of no better way to get a person to talk than by getting in a car and traveling through the country. At the sight of an intriguing or different barn, for example, any articulate person will mention something about it. And that something, then, is bound to lead to something else. As any good detective or bad crook learns, any single word uttered is a lead for the future. I began to be vaguely excited about a plan that was forming in my mind when Demara mentioned it himself.

"So you want to take me back to the scenes of my crimes?"

I told him I did and he hesitated for only a moment and then spun around on me.

"I like it," he said. "I'll do it. Now. Right now. I don't want to stop, I don't want to think about it, I want to go. Now!" Both of us were at a high pitch, but I, at the same time, was depressed.

How could I tell my wife? Not only would I be going out on the road with a man Judy increasingly felt was a dangerous madman, but our third baby was expected in about six weeks.

"I'm packed. Let's go," he said, and headed for the elevator.

There was nothing to do then but to simply stop at Perry Street, grab what clothes I could and face Judy with the facts. Secretly, I hoped she would be out with the children. Outside, under the hotel awning, Demara tipped the doorman a lavish sum; he was in a glowing, expansive mood, although the man hadn't helped us with the bags.

What a blessing I had the car parked outside, I thought.

"Where's the car?" he asked. I pointed to it. It was less than fifty feet away, but he appeared not to see it. I told him to wait and I would pull the car up to where the bags were.

Once again the car started up nicely. It often didn't. It was an old car but a good one. It was a 1950 black Pontiac and it had over 100,000 miles on it, and almost every one of them showed in one way or another. Although the car had never been involved in a major crash, it had had its share of minor ones. I had never had the dents repaired, but time is a healer. The rust from the dents after a while had blended into the over-all color scheme of the car and rendered all but the deepest dents unnoticeable.

The most serious drawback was that the car drastically lost power on hills, a problem of geriatrics. A secondary drawback was that the car had been hit in the back a few years before and the trunk was caved in as a result. I had solved this problem by using the back seat to carry two spare tires, luggage and children. The children seemed to like it, although I never found an adult who thought much of it.

When I drove up to the awning Demara did not appear to see me. I drove the Death Wagon (the family name for the car) directly up in front of him, and when he still didn't respond I opened my window so that my face was about two feet away from his.

"Fred, what's the matter?" I said. "It's me."

He stared at my face as if I were something that had come up out of the sidewalk and needed crushing.

"Oh, *no,*" he said, and he was in actual pain.

With the flat of his hand he dealt the car such a blow on the roof that I thought his fist was going to come down through.

"This will *never* do!"

He hit the Death Wagon once again causing people along 44th Street to turn and stare at us. My fear at the moment, beyond fear for the car, was that the hood would now begin to rise, a thing it often did when someone touched it the wrong way. The hood held.

"What do you think you're trying to do here?" he asked in a voice that made me feel cold inside. "I can't go this way."

The car, indeed, had never looked filthier. The pounding he had given it actually caused a cloud of dust and odd particles to float down from the inside of the roof.

"You don't seem to grasp some things about me," he said, with icy contempt. "I am used to traveling first class."

He paused to let that penetrate. When he was fully confident I had absorbed the message, he continued in the same tone. "In the event that it never dawned on you,"— he hit the car a last time—"that is *why* I do, *what* I do."

I was willing to admit defeat. Traveling first class was something that not only went against my grain, I never had been able to afford it in the first place. As long as the engine of the car was running I offered to take him to Penn Station. He had told me he was catching a ten o'clock train from there. Defeat wasn't that simple. Demara didn't even want to accept a free ride in the car. Just before I started up, however, he relented and walked around to the other side. He pulled on the handle and nothing happened. Some street vandals, no doubt after the tires piled in the back seat, had jimmied the handle in such a way that it now could only be opened from the inside. I leaned over to open it for him.

"It—ah, only opens from the inside," I said.

"Oh, *surprise*," he said.

I put his bags in back with the tires, and, although he got in, out of the corner of my eye I could see him gingerly perched on the edge of the seat as if contact with the upholstery might infect him with some loathsome blight. At 9th Avenue I headed the Death Wagon south and by this time the impostor had retreated into a kind of supernatural calm; he was as remote, as immovable, as stonily cold as a glacier. At a light I mentioned that we had only eight more blocks to go, but he didn't appear to hear me.

I don't know where I got the nerve to do what I did next. As we closed in on the station I began to maneuver the car over to one side to go down the ramp leading to an unloading platform, and although I very perceptibly slowed down, he did not react at all.

"I think you better get your bags ready," I warned him. Nothing.

Which is when I did it.

I did not turn down into the ramp; I did not even drive up to one side of the building and stop. Instead, hovering stiffly over the wheel, trying to whistle very low and naturally, I drove right past the station.

I like to think I gave him his chance. At 23rd Street I said, "We passed Penn Station," and then continued southward.

We went down past 14th Street and down past Perry Street and from the avenue I could actually see the sun glinting off the windows of our house. I was expected back by then, and I had a childish kind of little vision that Judy had seen me from the window, watching the Death Wagon roll by. Then we went down into the myth of Greenwich Village and through it. I had no plan but to keep the car moving. I can swear that I had no desire, real or fancied, to turn the car into the mouth of the Holland Tunnel, which gaped and beckoned to me. But it was truly as if I no longer had any real control over my mind or hands; the car was steering me. I'd say that in any court, and I would hope that people would understand and believe me.

I was now only vaguely conscious of passing the line in the tunnel that divides New York from New Jersey and then of coming up into the sunlight and gas stations, the billboards and run-down houses, the trash heaps and abandoned lives and aromatic odors wafting across from the Jersey Meadows beyond that let one know one has at last arrived in the Garden State. I was only conscious of the hulk of a man who loomed so large, so silent and so hostile beside me.

Once into New Jersey, however, I had a plan. The nearest place to us where Demara had once served in any *major* imposition was in Erie, Pennsylvania, where he had lived as Doctor Robert French, Dean of the School of Philosophy at Gannon College. I had no exact idea of where Erie lay except that it must be on the Great Lakes and at the end of a canal. But I had the feeling that if I could somehow get him there, and if things went well there, I might salvage both the trip and the project. I was also convinced that my success in even getting that far lay in keeping the rhythm of the car, the steady progression forward, as relentless and inevitable as fate.

I recall little of the day; only the omnipresent, omnious shadow of him. I recall driving through Boonton, because that seemed to break us out into the country, and skirting around Lake Hopatcong in the Sparta Mountains. Sometime in the day we drove through Tranquility because I wanted to mention it but I didn't dare. I was aware that the day was taking on the properties of my guest. The sky was becoming heavily overcast. Banks of dark gray clouds dropped down and began clinging close to the crest of hills and as early as three o'clock I decided to drive with my headlights on. All that early afternoon we drove into the lowering gloom of rural New Jersey and Demara was as dour as the day.

Outside a town called Pellettown I essayed my first words.

"Old car runs like silk," I said, proudly.

The silence was eerie. A light rain had begun to fall and the stretches of woods through which we drove looked unbearably lonely. I felt so completely alone that I found myself welcoming the sight of an oncoming car as if it were a kind of silent friend or ally on the road. If only I could move or penetrate this sulking hulk at my side. The gas meter was showing close to empty and nightfall was closing in when Demara finally spoke. His voice was

deep and it was grave and completely emotionless.
"I am going to have to have you arrested for kidnapping," he said.

The shock of his voice, coming as it did from the stolid
gloom, caused me to almost drive the car off the road. It
was only as I was getting the car back under control that
the impact of what he had said reached me and I very
nearly lost control again.

"You took me across a state line against my will." The
voice was hard and cold and meaningful. "You have heard
of the Lindbergh laws. You're not too ignorant to be familiar with them. Are you?"

"No, sir," I said.

"Well, you've broken them." I realized that this wasn't
meant as a joke. "The penalty," he added, "is death."

As absurd as it might appear later, it appeared far from
absurd then.

"*Help!*" he roared. This time I came perilously close to
ditching the car.

"Watch the road," Demara demanded. "I was only
practicing. I want to be in good voice when the moment
comes."

There were things that I could do. I could abandon
the car. I could turn off up some back road and hope he
didn't try to hold me before I made a run for it. I could
ride it out. But my resolve was not only paralyzed by in-
decision, I was also close to being out of gas. I entertained
a faint hope that I might find an isolated station where
I could get gas and where Demara might have a difficult
time getting the help he wanted. Somewhere near the
Pennsylvania border I found the place.

It was a two-tank, decrepit station, a Depression day survivor; and beyond my best hopes, out of the little shack, scrunching painfully along on the gravel leading to the car, came a man who must have been wizened and almost incapable even during that Depression many years ago.

I asked for two dollars worth of regular since it seemed the quickest and easiest way; I didn't want him to have to scrunch back and make change. And then I didn't relish the thought of being taken by the New Jersey police with a full tank of gas. With my heart thudding heavily and my breath coming in hard gasps, I watched Demara out of the corner of the rear-view mirror. He made no move of any kind. The old pump was taking a terrible length of time to register two dollars worth of gas. When it finally did, the old man came around to the windows with his cleaning rag.

"Skip the windows," I commanded, fluttering the two dollars at him, but he didn't heed me. Agonizingly, stubbornly, he began moving his somewhat greasy rag over the glass.

"Here's your money," I called out, but he looked at it scornfully and went around the car to go to work on the impostor's window. He wiped the window and I could see the old man goggling in at Demara who was goggling back at him. Demara gripped his throat with his hands and began turning red.

"Get help!" he suddenly shouted. *"I'm being kidnapped!"*

The old man wiped on. He even stepped back once and flicked a stubborn bug off the glass with his finger.

"Call the police!" Demara shouted through the glass

at the man. It was my enormous fortune that the right-hand window didn't work. *"I am being held a prisoner!"* The last was more like a wail than a shout.

The old man was at last completely satisfied with his work. He examined what he had done and he saw that it was good. He came around to the front of the car then and took my limp two dollars. Through my window Demara shouted at the man once again that he was being kid-napped.

When he had pocketed the money, the old man sud-denly began to move back across the gravel with an amazing speed, shifting sidewise like a wounded crab on the run, until he reached his little house. He went inside and locked the door and then one by one all the lights in the station and then the shack were flicked off until we were left, speechless, in complete darkness.

I didn't know what to do. Several times I saw the old man pull back a leather curtain and peep around it at us and finally it occurred to me that, for the time being, I was free to go. I had shifted the car into gear and slowly moved back out onto the highway when I heard a wheez-ing and chuffing which sounded as if something had gone drastically wrong with the engine. It was just my luck, my fitting fate, and then I realized that Demara was making the noise. When I looked at him, I first thought he was throwing a fit or enduring a seizure of some kind but at last he erupted in a gargantuan, thunderous roar of laughter. He pounded his knees and then he hit his head against the dashboard, he gulped and gasped and then roared again.

"Oh, God help us all, God help us all," he managed.

"The look. That *look*." He was rumbling as if a gush of lava were about to erupt. "Oh, God, that beautiful, pitiful, pie-eyed, petrified *look* on your face," he cried, and then tears began cascading down over the crimson of his cheeks.

"A stupid thing, *stupid*," I muttered. I found that I was still huddled over the wheel, presenting the smallest possible target.

"I will never forget that look in all my lives," he said, and that broke him up for a considerable time longer. When it seemed that he could at last talk, which he could do only by fits and starts, I asked him how he had dared fool with kidnapping. Out of his large, stuffed wallet he pulled a little packet of documents, and I turned on the overhead light. The papers, and a badge, complete with picture and fingerprints, established Demara, under a name I've now forgotten, as a special deputy sheriff from an upstate county in New York. If we had been stopped, and Demara was as chagrined about not being stopped as I was relieved, he would simply tell the officers that he was bringing me in and I had acted a little crazy.

"And whose word do you think they would have taken? Yours, or a fellow cop's?"

When we drove over a little bridge, Demara pitched the packet of papers out of my window into the river below.

"There goes two good weeks of work," he sighed. "Ah, well, occupational hazard. I can't very well have those things on me when I'm going to a place where I'm known, now can I?"

He was in a gay mood by then and my own spirits rose and so I decided I had better take a chance then and tell him that somewhere along the way I had taken a wrong turn and now I didn't know where I was going. That caused him to bellow joyfully again.

"Good God, don't let a thing like that bother you," he said. "That's the story of my life."

We drove in silence for a while after that, and he became rather subdued. After a while he suggested that it might be a good idea if I turned on my lights again.

"Oh, I am sorry," I said. "My God, I might have gotten us killed."

"That might not have been such a bad idea. Anyway, I've been driving in darkness for twenty years."

He lit a cigarette and by the flicker of his lighter I could see that while his voice was sarcastic his eyes were sad, even innocent, a sight I had not seen before. We drove for a long time after that before he began to talk.

"I used to think that if you just kept going, sooner or later you got there. I really used to believe there was a road that sooner or later led to some kind of paradise on earth. I really did. I've learned better now."

We passed a road sign that announced—SCRANTON 16.

"See what I mean?" Demara said.

We stopped at a motel outside of Scranton. I had been so preoccupied that it was only when I went back to the car to get my own luggage that I remembered I had none. It was vital that I telephone home before the police were alerted to my disappearance, but I decided I would call when we went out to dinner; at the moment I was badly in need of a nap.

When I woke it was morning. Demara was already up and ready to go. He was propped up on his bed reading one of two books which I happened to have in the car and which I had wanted him to read. One was titled *True Tales from the Annals of Crime and Rascality,* a collection of St. Clair McKelway's pieces about crime and its committers for *The New Yorker;* the other, an intriguing book called *Why You Do What You Do,* is a brilliantly readable collection of essays dealing with basic psychoanalytical problems which would aid even the densest and dullest to get some enlightened insight into the dark inner recesses of their minds and souls. Demara was, of course, reading the book on crime and rascality.

"These fools," he said. "They all get caught." I said that the only way the writer could do the book would be to use people who got caught.

"Well, I *don't* get caught. That's the difference between me and the others. Know why?" I dutifully asked why.

"The trouble with crooks is that they act like crooks and they look like crooks. That's the trouble with most cops, too. But if I ever do something wrong, it's someone *else* doing it."

I told him it was the other book that I really wanted him to read.

"The day I open that book is the day I cease being what I am," Demara said. "I don't want to know why I do what I do. I might not like what I find out."

A minute later he added, "I don't *want* to know who I am. I might not like him when I meet him."

At breakfast, in a diner out along the highway facing the stark, deserted maw of an empty mine, I took my first notes, but he made me put the notebook away. So for the rest of the journey I was forced to make all kinds of spurious stops and sneak into a fantastic variety of men's toilets in order to put down something I felt was important.

"I'm worried about your kidneys," he told me later. "I'd have them checked on when you get back."

"Yes, doctor," I said. Of course, he knew about the green notebooks into which I put all the straight, direct documentary notes, but with his ability to delude himself these books didn't bother him as long as he didn't see them. However, I didn't think he suspected the presence of a small, orange, plastic-covered notebook into which I put only my most wild and personal guesses about the sources and motivations of Demara's conduct. I didn't want him to find out about it, but on the second day out he did and its existence was to develop into a constant source of irritation and abrasion for the rest of the journey.

Scranton, Pennsylvania, as almost everyone knows, is one of the most depressing-looking cities in the world. In the space of little more than a hundred years it has managed to make itself look older and more decrepit, more unlivable and more corrupt than the slums of Rome and Paris have done in hundreds of years at much less cost. Almost everything in Scranton looks like it is going to come apart today or came apart yesterday.

"I love towns like this," Demara said. "I love it here." He sampled his breakfast. "Notice the food. Just the right soupçon of machine oil mixed in with a pinch of coal dust to give the eggs that good, authentic dying mill-town flavor."

As we left the diner, Demara said, "You have to have

an instinct for towns like these. You have to be decadent; you have to be rotten clean through to like this. This is important now," he said. "This is a thing you're going to have to learn about me if you're going to do this book right. I am rotten—rotten clean through."

"Ah, Fred," I said.

"Don't give me that," he ordered, harshly.

It is almost impossible to get to Erie properly; there is no right place to reach Erie from. You must sidle toward it and approach it on a slant. When we finally did get there it was dark, and Demara refused to enter the city at night.

"Do you think I want to risk being recognized there tonight and have it said that I came crawling back under the cover of darkness?"

We stayed in a motel outside of the city—"Relax From the Tensions of the Big City," the sign announced—and while we waited for our dinner in a highway restaurant I finally managed to telephone my wife.

"It's Daddy," I heard her call to the children. "And you're alive, you're alive," she said. "Are you free? Is he holding you? Can you talk? Speak to me."

I told her I would if I had the chance. I had a very difficult time explaining to her that I was all right, that Demara was not forcing me to say the correct things at gun point, that I wasn't being kidnapped (this was a piece of irony to relish), and that I wasn't in pain. She was, right at that time, in the process of instituting a thirteen-state alert for me. A strange thing was happening all the while she was talking. An old man who looked remarkably like Rudyard Kipling kept banging on the

phone booth with his cane, and when I finally opened
it up he motioned to me that I must put the highball I
was holding on a shelf outside the booth.

"State law," he said. "No drinking in phone booths."

"Are you *drinking?*" Judy said.

"Not *that* way," I assured her.

When I had properly assured Judy I was all right and
had talked at great expense to the children—"Boat? Was
that what you said? You can say 'boat.' *Wonderful,* Robbie,
just wonderful. Oh, *coat,* I see—" When I finally managed
to hang up I had forgotten to ask Judy to send ahead
some clothes by Air Express, but I didn't dare call again.
And when I came out of the booth I got a second disap-
pointment. My glass was empty and the old man stood
there grinning at me wisely, reeking of whisky.

"See." He pointed at the glass. "I saved you from sin."

After dinner we took a cold walk along a little brook
that seemed to flow with rust from old bedsprings, and
Demara told me about his past life in Erie. As Doctor
French, and a dean in the college, he had had high hopes
of becoming a pivotal character in Erie and, eventually,
a political power. As a dean he could count on the inde-
pendent and egg-head vote; as a Catholic in a fairly strong
Catholic town he had that vote; and as a politician, Demara was sure he could be a winner. It was also rumored
that French was enormously rich, a rumor he himself had
begun.

"It is always wise to let people think you have money.
I don't care what you may say, unless you do something
dreadful, people think money and goodness go together.

Somehow God *has* to be on the side of the rich or how else would He tolerate them to be that way? It also assures you a nice measure of justice from the police. I know," he added.

But now he was afraid he had made a major mistake in coming back. He didn't know how to face the people he had fooled as French. Another thing held him back. The spiritual leader of Gannon is Bishop John Mark Gannon. While at Gannon College, in an inspired moment, Demara had tried to found (Demara has a tremendous drive to be the founder of something) a religious order for laymen called, nicely enough, the Pious Society of St. Mark. Demara had a good idea that the bishop was not going to let him get away with that one, no matter how many years had passed. In fact, Demara, over those years, had come to associate Bishop Gannon's name with the hot, rich scent of boiling oil.

"What makes me feel worst of all is that these people loved me here. I don't know how to act."

I told him that he had always found a way to act in the past and that he would just have to invent a way to act the next day.

"Invent," he said. "I like that. Yes, of course. I shall invent a way. Then I'll be all right."

We were back at the motel. The idea cheered him up. He went promptly and cheerily to sleep while I lay and thrashed and tossed the whole night through.

6.

All of the doubts of the night before vanished with the darkness. In the morning he was a new man. A great many of the attributes of Demara, his charm and poise and assurance, were still with him, but there was a new ingredient added to them. At times Demara appears to be acting. His poise in a crisis is an act, his charm with strangers too obviously the act of being charming. But now these mannerisms were genuine ones. The word was *effortless*.

It occurred to me that this must have been one of the guiding features of the impostor when he was on one of his hoaxes. As someone else, freed from himself, he has complete confidence that this new man can do what he needs or wants to do; he has never failed him like Demara has done. In this case, however, the switch was even more complex.

"They know Dr. French, they don't know Demara. So Demara can do anything, do you see?" he explained to me later.

This kind of complication occurs often when dealing with Demara.

The change was apparent at once. In the restaurant we got special service. There is a kind of man who, endowed with effortless assurance, seems to get all his questions answered. People want to answer him. There is another kind of person who almost never seems to get his questions understood, much less answered. I was beginning to feel that Demara was some kind of *grand seigneur* and I was his spear carrier, and the worst of it was that it was easy to take.

All the way downtown he excitedly pointed out things of interest about Erie. He pointed to the statue of Captain Gridley, the "You may fire when ready, Gridley" of Dewey and Manila Bay fame.

"Can you imagine a full-blown city whose biggest hero is a lanyard yanker?" he asked. The sight of the statue never failed to irk him. "I'll let you in on a secret about myself. With Gridley as the opposition, I always had a sneaking hope that if everything went right Dr. French might be up there."

Another irritation was a song titled "The Bells of Erie," written by Bishop John Mark Gannon, which rang out from every Catholic belfry in town quite a few times a day.

"The whole song has two notes in it and I've never been able to get it out of my head," he told me. "The Chinese water torture is a mild thing when stacked against 'The Bells of Erie.'"

We had come upon the college quicker than he had anticipated while talking and he was stunned by the changes that had taken place.

"What hath God and Gannon wrought," he said. "Look

what they've gone and done without me," he said in despair. For the moment his poise deserted him, and I could
see that despite the cold, blowy day, he was sweating.

"Why don't you have a drink first?" I asked him, and
this made him angry. Next I meekly suggested that he
didn't *have* to go into the school. This angered him even
more.

"What kind of person do you take me for," he glowered
at me. "I have a duty to perform."

He straightened himself as best he could and then
stepped out of the car.

"We're going in," he said.

Once on the sidewalk he threw his shoulders back and
spun on his heels. His plaid tie had worked itself loose
from his jacket and now it fluttered in the wind back up
over his shoulder like a Highlander's battle tartan on
parade. With me trailing him a good distance behind,
Ferdinand Demara advanced on his old college as if he
were going to demand its surrender.

I felt that a peek or two inside some of the buildings and
a chat with a few old-timers by myself would prove enough
for our needs, but I hadn't reckoned with the impostor.
He once told me that one of the secrets of good impostoring was a flair for going all the way.

"If you ever start to do something, then you are committed to it; you've got to do it all the way up to the
hilt."

He was as good as his axiom.

At the door of the first classroom we passed, Demara
did not knock; he flung it open.

"Good morning, Professor," Demara boomed.

Every head turned in our direction.

"Just one of the old boys coming back to see how things are coming along. Carry on, sir. Pay no attention to us."

The room was a combination laboratory and lecture room. We took seats in the back of the hall and for several minutes maintained a respectful silence. Then Demara began making low-voiced but pointed comments about the quality of the training as compared to that of his day. He leaned across his seat to a row of students in front of us.

"Not like my day at all, not at *all*," he said. The students turned respectfully.

"Do you know that we had a full professor here who had never even graduated from high school?"

The students appeared dubious.

"It's true. One of those self-educated geniuses." He turned to me. "You remember his name, don't you?" he said, and I vigorously nodded no.

"He was a good man. Sound. Capable," Demara said. "But weak in the classics. Small Latin and less Greek."

We got up to leave.

"Splendid work in here. Splendid," the impostor said. "Carry on."

Everyone seemed to glow with good feeling as we swept out.

After that we strolled with complete calm all through the school buildings and around the college grounds. The college is in rather a strangulated position. Although thirsting to expand, it finds itself checked and blocked from all sides, a kind of intruder in the enemy camp. On one side it is stymied by the County Court House and

the First Presbyterian Church, on another by Perry
Square, a large, public park, on a third it is flanked by the
Cathedral and buildings of the Cathedral of St. Paul
(Episcopal), and to the west, lurking down on Sassafras
Street, lies the First Church of Christ, Scientist. The end
result is that Gannon is parceled out in chips and pieces
all over the Erie landscape, a true challenge to archi-
tects' ingenuity. Unless the Protestant faith collapses in
our time, or comes over to the Roman Catholic side again,
the future of a unified campus for Gannon must always
remain a chimera.

Demara was not afraid of being spotted. He has another
axiom, which he believes in thoroughly, that people do not
spot you unless they are looking for you. A guiding rule is
to always act as if you belong to wherever you are. His
belief is that people are so insecure in this present world
that they never feel they belong, even when they do. If you
act as if you belong almost no one will question you.

We marched up the stairs into what had once been the
manor house of the school, a great, gilded, oak-paneled
Victorian mansion that once had belonged to one of
Erie's wealthiest families and which had been the heart
of the college when Demara presided there.

"Now, if I'm going to be recognized, it's here," he
warned me. "But I won't be."

We went into the ornate, primly lavish main room
and stopped briefly while Demara tried to get his bear-
ings. While we stood there several people passed and eyed
us curiously, but that would happen in any college, and
several others asked if they could be of help.

"Is **Dr.** Robert French still associated with the

school?" Demara asked a woman at a reception desk. She claimed that she had never heard of the man.

"That was a stupid thing to do. You might have ruined our whole stay here," I said.

"Wouldn't you have asked her? Just to see what she'd say?" I told him no.

"Then that is just the difference between you and me," he said. We started up a flight of stairs two at a time, moving with a sense of purpose.

"We're not supposed to be up here but no one will stop us. That belonging business, you know."

He showed me the room where he had once lived and then back downstairs he showed me the wall which had seen some of his least fine hours. Monsignor Wehrle, the head of the college in Demara's day, had owned a large, fierce Norwegian elk hound which had taken a dislike to Demara.

"He smelled a phony," Demara admits.

To get even with the dog Demara had devised a cruel scheme. He would tie up the hound at one end of the marble-floored hall and at the other put some fresh red beef. After allowing the dog to slaver for a good length of time he would then release the animal. The beast would roar across the marble, put on the brakes in front of the meat, and go slamming and skidding into the wall.

"He never learned," Demara said. "And neither did I."

It was because of the dog that Demara finally was ordered to leave Gannon, which he loved.

"If your boss has a dog, ignore the boss until you get that dog to love you. Once you have the beast on your side, the boss is a cinch to follow."

An amazing thing to me about so many of Demara's axioms for impostors is that, while they seem to buoy him up, they so often don't work. Yet he might go mad without them.

We were treading our way on a narrow walk between two buildings when I felt Demara stiffen and heard him take a quick intake of air.

"Oh, this could be bad," he said.

We were recognized.

Ahead of us, coming directly toward us on the walk, was an elderly man. Even from the distance we were from him I could make out the fact that he knew the face and was merely trying to recall the name. I felt sure he would have it when he reached us.

"I'll cover for you," I said. "Get behind me."

But instead of turning away, I felt Demara move past me and saw him bear down on the old man like an ocean liner moving in on a hapless rowboat.

"Where's the new gym?" Demara demanded, almost in a growl. The man was startled. "And don't give me a bum steer like the other guy."

The man gently turned and pointed back the way we had come.

"Then how come the other guy said 'Back there'?" Demara said, and he spun the man around. The man didn't know.

"Why should I take your word?" he demanded. The man simply insisted that the gym was in the direction he pointed.

"You're sure?" Demara said.

"I'm certain. Believe me," the man pleaded.

"You're not trying to string me along?"

"I promise," the man vowed. Demara turned to me. "Think I ought to trust him?" I said I thought so. "We're going to trust you," he told the man, and the man seemed enormously relieved. "But it better be there."

"Oh, it will be, it will be," the man said. I swore he was going to add "unless they moved it today," but he stuck to his ground. We abruptly took leave of the man, but when we were nearly through the passageway Demara called back to him that it better be there or we would come looking for him. When he was out of sight I attacked Demara, for the first time daring to be critical of him.

"That was a mean thing to do," I said. He was very hurt by that.

"Good God, do you think I wanted to do that? That I liked doing it? I used to love that old man once." I asked him why he did it then.

"Why, Foch's law." He took a dramatic posture. "When your left is crumbling, when your right is about to give, when the center cannot hold—I attack."

He went on to explain the maneuver in depth. Take this case! Had Demara taken the defensive it would by now almost certainly be all over Gannon, if not Erie, that the famous fake, Dr. French, was back. But he had so confounded and confused the old man that the identification became secondary. He mainly hoped we found the gym and weren't coming looking for him. He might even tell his wife that the odd thing was that the man looked like that old Dr. French but he would not make that the main issue. Furthermore, Dr. French would have known where the gym was. Only a stranger would not know.

A second opportunity to bring Foch's law into operation occurred barely a half-hour later. We were standing on French Street, appropriately enough, deliberating where to have lunch, when I saw her coming across the street. There was no doubt in my mind that she had made an identification, but I didn't signal Demara since I felt I had better watch him wheel his artillery into action.

She touched him on the arm. "Dr. French," she said. "As I live and breathe. What brings you back to Erie?"

It was horrible what he did to her and I writhed inside, embarrassed for myself and feeling sorry for her. With Foch as his guide, he chopped her assault into shreds. He accused her of unaccountable rudeness, he let her know that this was the sixth time some idiot had stopped him that day alone, and he finally asked her quite seriously where she learned her bad manners. The woman merely wanted to run. She did. She fled.

"Now, that, of course, was a little more severe. But then she was a more dangerous case. Women always are," he added.

After lunch, while he stirred his fifth spoonful of sugar into his coffee he told me that he had hated doing that to the woman.

"But if you're going to be an impostor, you can't worry about people's sensibilities; you've got to *use* them. You can only worry about your own. Another occupational hazard," he said, philosophically.

After lunch he showed me another facet of the impostor's technique. This one, an extension of Foch's theory, involves seizing the high ground or taking the initiative before an attack is even launched. Although it was cold and blustery we took a walk down to Lake Erie and on the way we stopped into a snuggery where Demara, as French, had whiled away many a beery hour.

"I know, I know, I know," he said, as we went in through the door, "I look like Dr. French. Will you do me a favor and not mention that name to me? Will you promise? I'm going out of my mind in this town."

"Well, you *do* look like him," the bartender said.

Demara grabbed his head and groaned. "I told you. Didn't I tell you?" he said to me.

The ritual was continued for several minutes while it was laboriously discussed how much Demara really did look like French and sound like French until it was finally mentioned that French was some kind of crook or nut, and Demara took severe umbrage at being compared to a nut and the conversation dwindled at last. The secret here is to be so open, so bold and forward that suspicion becomes indecent.

"If I went in there tomorrow and insisted I was Dr. French, they'd throw me out of the place," he said.

In the afternoon we went back to the college and in several places I was sure he was identified. We also continued to go to places where we were not supposed to go and were never asked to leave. The whole performance saddened Demara.

"I'm going to let you in on the big secret of my business now," he said to me that day. "The main reason I don't get caught, even when people begin to suspicion me highly, even when sometimes they begin to suspect that an impostor is educating their own children, is that

they don't want to be unnice. It's not that they don't want
to butt in. Oh, they'll butt in all right in this age of com-
mittees and conformity. Don't fret about that. But they
want to be *nice*. This is what I operate on. I'll *let* you
write this one down. Here it is: Most Americans would
rather be liked than right."

He said he thought that that was one of the troubles
with this country and it was growing worse. It is one of his
contentions that as an impostor he wouldn't last a week in
England, where people hold their inner convictions with
more honor.

I was sorry that I wasn't able to meet or talk to any
of the old Gannon people but that was impossible as long
as Demara stayed with me and Foch's law was operating. I
also began to think that he didn't want me to talk with
anyone who knew him as someone else. I was going
to have to sneak around a bit.

We went back to the motel, where I changed into the
first of many shirts I was to buy en route, and then went
back to the restaurant where my drink was stolen. Rudyard Kipling was there. I asked Demara, as a favor to take
his drink into the phone booth and, puzzled, he did.
The old codger attacked and then I saw him retreat empty-
handed.

"How did you do that?" I asked him. The fellow had
been terribly persistent with me.

"I told him," Demara said, "that I had just placed a
call to state police barracks that a man was molesting me
in a phone booth."

"And that," I said, "is the difference between you
and me."

"Well, it was the truth, wasn't it?"

I agreed.

"Always stick to the truth, Crichton, until it becomes inconvenient."

In the morning, after another tour of Gannon during which Demara wrote *F. W. Demara was here. Does anyone care?* and *Dr. Robert French will lecture on logic tomorrow* on several black boards, I checked out and found the motel price reduced to eight dollars. I didn't argue the point but I mentioned it later to the impostor.

"Why, of course," he said, "professional rates," and then told me what he had done. He had gone to the office, re-registered himself as Dr. French and let it be known that, now that he was coming to Gannon, a stream of international scholars could be expected to start coming into Erie. He suggested that if professional rates were extended, a good many of those scholars might be persuaded to use the motel's facilities.

I asked him how he had explained me.

"I told him what you were. I said you were my biographer. He was very much impressed. He said you looked like a biographer. The price, of course, plummeted at once."

We sidled out of Erie heading, at first, south and west, trying to get away, which can be as hard as getting in.

"You really are a bastard," I said.

"Oh, I am," Demara said, pleased.

"No," I said, seriously. "You *really* are a bastard."

"Now you're *getting* it," he said excitely. "Hold on to it, clutch it to you, never let it get away."

We drove in silence for a long time while I pondered

all the lessons I had learned in Erie. Something about the stay there still seemed incomplete, and then it occurred to me that in all my time there I never heard "the bells."

"Oh, yes, you did. You heard them. They're now a part of you. What's that word . . . subliminal? 'The Bells of Erie' are a part of you and you can't shake them." He put his head against the right window, now a favorite posture of his, pressed his forehead against the pane and reflected aloud. "One night you're going to wake up and those bells are going to be ringing and you're going to become terribly sad. They're going to make you sad for all the things you did and all the things you never did. You'll get up and you'll wander around the room and you won't be able to stop the sad ringing of those bells."

I felt he was being dramatic although I was beginning to have no doubts now that the impostor was often haunted by his past.

"Then you know what you do?" he asked. "You decide you had better get up and get dressed and do something, anything, right away or the sound of those bells will drive you mad."

A little after that, he said another revealing thing.

"They'll drive you mad if you have a soul so it pays not to have one, see? I'm trying to lose my own and then the bells won't bother me."

7.

Something was bothering Demara deeply. An inner war was being waged inside his mind, but what factions were fighting and which was winning I didn't know. It was forbidden to discuss such things. So we just drove.

"Let's go in search of grime," Demara had said and I headed the car back toward the hard and soft coal fields. There is a kind of grim beauty in good, honest grime, as many artists have discovered.

Before getting into the coal country, however, we stopped at a wolf farm on the top of a mountain. The farm was run by an old doctor whose goal was to preserve the last pack of big, fierce lobo wolves in the east. Now near the end of his days it was told to us that he had asked the state to take over the pack but that the state wasn't interested. In response to that it is said that the old man's last gesture is going to be to open the gates and give the state the lobos whether they want them or not. It will be a dark day for Pennsylvania when thirty-five or forty full-grown wolves begin to roam their northern hills.

I went over to a part of the fenced-in yard where a huge specimen lay panting and as I neared the deceptively thin

looking mesh that kept the animal in, the wolf, with a
frightening snarl, hurled himself against it. I jumped in
fright and let out an involuntary gasp.

"Now watch me," Demara said.

Slowly, with complete confidence and with great delib-
erateness he moved toward the wolf, holding its eye with
his own, talking to it with a soothing voice until he was
within eating distance of the animal. He squatted by the
animal, talking to it, and then turned to me.

"He recognizes another member of the underworld.
We're the outsiders, the misfits in the civilized world."

Later he told me that exactly that same technique and
approach accounted for his spectacular success as a prison
warden. Even though Demara was a "screw" and, as such,
officially an untouchable, the prisoners responded to him
because beneath all the trappings they recognized a kin-
dred soul.

There was no question that the wolf failed to accept me
and later in Texas I failed to get contact with any of the
prisoners I talked to. To them I was the enemy, a member
of the institution they couldn't join and which they in
turn despised. But Demara could talk to lobo wolves.

We drove down through the anthracite country. Coal
corrupts a countryside and hard coal corrupts absolutely.
We passed the first slag piles, some of them smoking from
fires which have burned deep inside them for years, and
the first mine faces and coal camps, and Demara seemed
unusually pleased. The further we went, the better the
grime grew. Spring is a good time for grime. Patches
of black snow still clung to the raped and ruptured hill-
sides and in the streams black chunks of rotting ice jostled

their way downstream in cold, coal-black waters. In the towns coal dust, the spume and brine of the coal country, had settled on top of mounds of snow and then frozen there so that the piles looked like gray, greasy boulders made from some artificial substance.

When we reached the Shenandoah Valley—the one where the apple blossoms don't bloom and tourists never come—we turned down into it. Tourists should come, because there is no sight in the world that can equal the alternate ugliness and depraved beauty of Shamokin, or the feel of decay and decline of Kulpmont and Shenandoah, cities cringing in the valley bottoms, humbled by preposterous overhanging mountains of culm. Humbled now by the slag, the slate, the slack, the waste and the dregs, wrenched from the bowels of the earth—all of these things which once enriched them and which now, in their want, degrades them.

"They should save one of these towns," Demara said. "They should make it into a National Park. Then people who think they have nothing to live for could come here. They'd go away shouting for joy that they don't have to stay here."

We decided that it would be a national rejuvenation center. It would be called *So You Think* You *Got It Bad National Park.*

He studied the faces of the people we saw in the towns with an open intensity and I had the feeling that he was trying to find some vestige of himself in the faces. He had grown up in a dying mill town, the decaying textile center of Lawrence, Massachusetts, and one of his rarely voiced theories about his own conduct was that he was spending the rest of his lives trying to compensate for it. Demara harbors a strange belief that anyone who remains in towns like these and voluntarily raises their children in them is corrupt.

We drove to the town of Jim Thorpe, Pennsylvania, which was named a few years ago after the great Oklahoma Indian football player who played for the Carlisle Indian School when that little college took on the greatest teams in America, such as the great Harvard teams, and whipped them. The original name of the town had been Mauch Chunk which Demara felt, and I do, is one of the inspired names for a coal town. We had an interesting exchange on a street corner.

"Why did you do it? Why did you change the name?" Demara demanded of a group of men lounging in the sun outside a diner. The old name had no class we were told and someone related how a native had gone on a nationally televised quiz show and when he said where he came from the audience sniggered.

"See? No class!"

"As compared with Jim Thorpe," Demara said, acidly.

"That's right," a lounger said. "A great ball player."

"Not to mention high jumper," someone added.

"You couldn't I suppose have picked someone of some real achievement?" he asked. We were answered with incredulous stares.

"Six touchdowns in seven carries isn't achievement?" a man asked.

We drove away.

"They deserve themselves," Demara said. Later he said: "I'm getting depressed. Our gods grow tinier and tinnier and more remote. You watch. Someday someone will try and make a hero out of me. Then you'll know the nation is sick unto its death."

All was not a complete loss, however. We went through the town of Tamaqua and Demara decided that it was the ideal name.

"File this name away," he ordered. "Someday I'm going to come from here."

With this name we perfected what has since become known as The Test of Tamaqua; a literary axiom. If a literary title is to be important or lasting or effective, it must be able to absorb the name Tamaqua. There is some truth in it.

It works this way. Thomas Wolfe's novel, *Of Time and the River* becomes *Of Time and the Tamaqua*. It is improved; it is a great title.

I thought of Hemingway's *Tamaqua in the Afternoon*, *The Green Tamaquas of Africa* and of *How Green Was My Tamaqua*, all good. But Demara felt I was only transposing and not using Tamaqua creatively. I admit several of his had a flair mine might have lacked. He came up with:

Paul Bunyan and His Great Blue Tamaqua. Praise the Lord and Pass the Tamaquas and, the prettiest perhaps, *For Whom the Tamaqua Tolls.*

But I like to feel that in the long run, by plugging away at it, as compared to his flashy approach, that I found the best. The original belongs to Huxley.

After Many a Tamaqua Dies the Swan.

After Tamaqua we tired of grime, and we finally managed to escape it and drive into the ordered, spotless, richly endowed world of the Plain People—the Mennonites and Amish. We took the traditional tour through Bird-In-Hand, Intercourse, Paradise, Blue Ball and back up to Ephrata, driving sadly through the country fat with well-loved loam, the fields glowing freshly green with spring wheat, the big barns fatly white and red, hexed barns, and the whole country gauzed over with an early spring fume. It was almost preposterous to think that only thirty miles away was the black despair of the coal people.

"What destroys me, what kills me," Demara said, "is that I know that if I lived here, in three months I'd be back up in that coal country because that's the only place I'd feel I would belong. What a real fraud."

We continued to drive aimlessly and then I had the sharp feeling that the battle inside Demara, if not settled, had reached the cease-fire stage.

With great bravado he said, "Let us hie to Punxsutawney." It had—it has, a gallant ring about it.

I had always wanted to go to Punxsutawney if only to send some friends postcards reading: Wish YOU were here.

The road to Punxsutawney, like the road to hell, needs mending. If you ever are traveling from Bird-In-Hand to Punxsutawney, be sure to carry a spare. The trip took us much longer than we expected and we arrived when most of the town was shuttered up and its people tucked away in their goose-feather mattresses. In a drugstore I watched Demara get an address from a phone book and then ask directions. When he came out, he directed me to what appeared at night to be the rectory of a Roman Catholic church.

"I won't be long," he said.

He crossed the yard at a trot and bounded up the steps of the house and reached for the bell. But just as he was about to ring it, he faltered. He stood in front of the door for a long time and then came back down. He turned again and repeated the performance. Finally he came back to the car.

"All right, you don't have to sit there and *watch* me, for Christ's sake," he bellowed. After a time he tried it again, and again he failed.

"O.K., put it in your orange notebook. Write it down but let me tell you one thing. Whatever you put in there is *wrong*."

A little while after this show he asked me why didn't I get lost, didn't I have any manners, and I suddenly stormed out of the car. I had been sitting there planning to walk downtown and bring us back something to eat since I gathered he felt he had to wait there and see someone, but that was the breaking point.

"I hope you starve," I shouted at him, and started walking toward the few lights of the town. I had the key so I had no fear he might leave me stranded in Punxsutawney. I had a nice leisurely dinner washed down with steins of local beer and then I went to a movie. The miracle of the movies in a small town never fails to excite me. To come off a quiet shady street in a little farm town and step into the dark wonder of a world peopled with Ingrid Bergman is a luxury of life that should not be taken for granted.

After the movie I went to a local tavern and drank beer and was astonished to experience a wave of rural cynicism. The people all stopped talking to watch the television program, "21," on which Charles Van Doren rose and fell, and to a person they were convinced that the program was rigged and fixed. They were right, but the cynicism of America is a thing that puzzles me and Demara understands well.

It was such a blessing, such a treat to stand up to a bar and order ice-cold beer without the hulking shadow of the impostor hovering over me, watching my moves critically, that I stayed drinking until they closed the place. Just before I left I put through an exuberant call to Judy.

"Punxsutawney?" she said. "What in the world are you doing in Punxsutawney?"

I didn't know, of course, and I had to tell her that, and she started crying, for reasons I couldn't seem to grasp.

"I want you to come home. At once. This night," she demanded. "I'm going to have my baby ahead of time. I know I am. I can feel it. And, Bob. I'm afraid of that man."

"I'm not. He's just a big fat lout," I said. Even with all the beer in me I knew I was lying.

When I went out on the street, Punxsutawney was reeling. But I was happy and I had the good fortune to witness one of the finer manifestations of brotherly love. Along the street ahead of me the door to another tavern opened and two men struggled out of the place.

"Can't let you drive home *that* way," one man said.

"Goddamn, *gonna* drive," the other replied.

"Turn your head, Tom," the first man said, and when Tom obliged he proceeded to knock him down with a smashing blow to the jaw. When Tom clambered off the ground, he was knocked down again until he just lay there.

"You won't like me for this until tomorrow, Tom," he said humbly. He dragged the body over the sidewalk and dumped it into the back seat of a car.

"My brother-in-law," the man explained to me. "Get hisself killed if he drove. He'll be fine in the morning." He got in his car. "I like the man, only trouble is he's getting to hate me. But Jane, she asks me to do it. That's my sister and it would be a sorry man who wouldn't help his sister when she needs it. Right?"

"Right," I agreed, and then he roared away into the night.

When I got back to the car, Demara appeared not to have moved. He sat as before, his eyes riveted on the front door of the rectory. For a long time we sat in silence.

"Don't you ever do that again," he said.

"Do what?"

"Don't you ever *dare* to do that again."

I had no idea what he meant.

"Don't you ever go off and desert me like that again. Walking off and leaving me without a word."

"I'm sorry," I said. I really did feel sorry for him. I promised that I wouldn't do it again and then, as sleep overwhelmed me, had to announce that I had to desert him again.

"Go ahead," he said, "I'm glad to be rid of you," but his voice was different.

It was still dark when I woke in the morning, but the

thin grayness of approaching dawn was on the horizon. I was stiff and cold, but he was still sitting there as before. I told him he had better get in the back seat and curl up with the tires, but he refused the offer. He looked terrible and I finally forced myself to ask him why we were there.

"If you weren't so dense I should gather that you would have gathered that I am here to pay my respects to someone."

"So you're back to insulting me again," I said. A hangover has some value in that one often doesn't really give a damn.

"Insulting?" he said. "You must have the skin of a baby. Besides," he said, in the sudden revealing way he so often has, "you know you have the upper hand." He nodded in the direction of the orange notebook in my pocket. "You'll always have the last word, but what do I have to defend me but what I can get away with?"

I went downtown for coffee and rolls and when I got back Demara was beaming.

"Thanks for your patience," he said. "It's all right now. I saw him, the finest man I ever knew."

Like the deacon's masterpiece, he all at once collapsed in every piece. He climbed over into the back seat, thumped down on the tires and a bag, and scrunched under an old army blanket I had back there. He was in such good spirits and so vulnerable that I decided to attack then. I was developing my own Foch laws.

"You know, I do have to learn something about you sometime," I said.

"Aren't you the opportunistic bastard," Demara

laughed. "All right. One question." He knew what it was going to be, of course. I had to know the name of that man.

He paused for a very long time.

"His name is Alexander McComb Kinkaide. He's the person who first helped me turn toward the religious life. If I have a conscience, it's Alexander Kinkaide. If I have a soul, it's his. No matter what I do in this world I always wonder what he would say about it."

I felt elated. I had stumbled on a nugget of pure gold and I tucked it away in my mental gold-dust bag for future spending. Now all I had to do when the trip was over was to contact this Alexander McComb Kinkaide and have a long, rewarding talk with him.

It is a lovely name, a euphonious one and one that harmonizes in all its parts. It was perfect for a man of religion I felt. And so it became one of the shocks of my life to learn weeks later that there was no such person as Alexander McComb Kinkaide.

I never found out who the real man was. Whoever he is, however, he does, as did the fictitious Kinkaide, exert a profound influence on the impostor. From simply viewing him, the internal war was over. I felt a surge of renewed strength in Demara and a feeling of calm I had never seen in him before.

"Now on to the walls of Gethsemani," he ordered, and he fell into a deep sleep.

8.

It was early afternoon when the impostor finally woke. He rose up from the back seat, the old blanket draped over his head like a prayer shawl, as if he were climbing out of the sea. For a moment he sat there seeing nothing, rubbing the sleep from his puffy eyes, but then the world got through to him.

"Oh no," he said, "not this again."

We were back in the coal country. The car was grinding its way up the steep main street of a semi-abandoned coal town. Unpainted miners' shacks, standing on stilts, limped like cripples up the hill alongside us. Near the top the asphalt, pitted and rutted, ended entirely and it was plain to see we were climbing a mountain of culm. At the crest stood a collection of coal-blackened stores, many of them closed, whose windows stared bleakly back at us as we passed.

"Stop!" Demara ordered. At first I didn't believe him.

"*Stop!*" he ordered again. I drove just over the top of the hill so the car would be sure of starting again and stopped. We looked at the broken windows of the deserted stores but even sadder were the stores still open for business. Everything in the windows had a sun-bleached look, like stale candy in a cheap candy store, which coal dust had then blackened.

"You're serious?" I said.

"I'm serious. They need the trade," he said.

We got out of the car. With me following well in the rear, he marched up the cracked sidewalk and then stepped down a few stairs into the grimmest, toughest bar I had ever seen. A bitter line of coal-seamed faces looked up from their drinks and glared at Demara as he advanced upon them. Without exception they were taking their whisky neat with beer chasers.

"A very perfectly made dry martini, innkeeper, if you please," the impostor said, in a very imperfect English accent.

"A *what?*" the bartender growled. In the silence that followed the bartender moved down along the bar until he was directly in front of Demara.

"Look, Fatso," he said, tapping a bottle on the bar for emphasis, "whatever the hell it is—we ain't got it!"

I began moving backwards out of the doorway, feeling with my heels for the steps, hoping I might draw Demara with me.

Demara waggled a finger at the bartender.

"Oh, yes you do," he said, with an innocent, smiling assurance. "Bring down that bottle there."

Everyone looked up at a shelf on which an ancient, dust-covered bottle of vermouth stood. The bartender's arm made a motion to reach for the bottle but then was withdrawn.

"That's right. That one," Demara said. The bottle of vermouth was reluctantly lifted down from the shelf.

"Now, a jigger, please," Demara commanded.

Into the jigger he poured a thick, dark-green fluid that resembled no vermouth I had ever seen. With every eye on him, he swished the liquid around in the little glass, leaned over the bar, and then abruptly tossed it down the drain.

"Aaaah," said the men.

"Now, then," Demara said. "I'll want a large glass of water with lots of ice. Lots," he said loudly.

The bartender muttered.

"Ice," he said, disbelievingly. For a moment he wavered and then started down the bar, went under the duck-under and into what must have been a kitchen. We heard the sound of an icebox door and then the sound of an ice pick brutally chipping away at a block of ice.

"Ice! He says he wants ice," we could hear him saying. Eventually a long glass of ice was produced and filled with water and Demara drank it down. I was relieved to see that the bartender did not still have the ice pick in his hand. Then he put the glass out onto the bar. The men were staring at the glass as if it were about to do something.

"More ice!"

It was produced this time with no muttering.

"And now, a jigger of gin," Demara said. The miners had moved down along the bar and were beginning to hunch forward.

"Another."

"And another."

"One more."

"Another might do it."

"And again."

At each command, his voice grew louder.

Soon, six jiggers of gin were lined up along the bar. Against the black, scarred surface of the bar the gin and the glass glittered with the pristine clarity of gems. Each of the jiggers of gin was poured, in turn, into the jigger that had once held the vermouth. Each was swished once around in the vermouth glass and then flipped into the tumbler of ice.

"Now, then, Boniface. The very largest glass you own."

After a good deal of mumbled debate along the bar, a huge, glass, beer stein, labeled "Bet You Can't," was produced from the back room. It was washed and dried and placed on the bar.

I was sent down the street to procure a lemon.

When I got back Demara had finished the ritual of stirring the drink—so many turns, ever so gently so as not to bruise the gin or insult the vermouth—and the mammoth martini was being poured into the glass stein in a crystal stream. He let the concoction sit in the glass until the fluid was motionless, holding out his hands for utmost silence. When there was no longer any movement, and no sound at all, he crowned the drink with a delicate twist of lemon peel.

For a brief moment Demara stepped back and admired what he had done. Then, while the miners hunched tensely and stared in awe, the great impostor raised the tankard on high.

"To the men who dig the coal," he said, and in one magnificent gesture the magnificent fraud emptied the stein.

"Ohhh," the men breathed.

In tribute they rose as a man and each took a belt of his boilermaker.

When quiet was restored, despite the fact that tears were streaming down his face, and that his face was an amazing red, and ignoring the fact that he was choking and wheezing, Demara managed to make his clincher.

"Gentlemen," he gasped. "This is an historic day."

The men leaned forward respectfully, the better to hear his voice, which by now was very low and very hoarse.

"You have just seen," he announced to them, "the first perfect martini ever made in East Glinty Glo, Pennsylvania."

There was a moment of silence again, followed by a spontaneous roar of applause.

As he turned to go Demara produced a ten-dollar bill, waggled it in the air to still the din and slid it onto the bar.

"For the men, host. A treat for the men."

With a wave, and a nod, he swept out.

Subdued, silent, we walked back to the car. The great performance was done and like the stein, we were drained. Silently we climbed in and Demara leaned back against the seat.

"It gives them, you see, a sense of belonging to a wider, richer world," he croaked—and fell fast asleep.

9.

"I'm in a rare mood, a stinging, stunning mood," Demara announced. Below us, beneath the bridge, the reddish water of the spring, flood-full Ohio ran to the Mississippi and ahead of us the dark black hills of Kentucky loomed.

We were at last on our way to the abbey of Our Lady of Gethsemani, the Trappist monastery in which the impostor had served as Frater French and which was brought to national attention by Thomas Merton in his book *The Seven Storey Mountain.*

"I'm full of great expectations," Demara said. "Who knows. Maybe they'll even let us stay there. They're very forgiving people, you know."

We had crossed into Kentucky and Covington and were in hilly Newport, a den of easy vice and iniquity, a sinkhole that has proved to be a blessing for staid Cincinnati. Newport and environs allows that stolid city of solid burghers to boast of its high morals, its fine police force and its low crime rate; when anyone really wants to act up he is simply enticed across the river into sinful Kentucky. This allows Cincinnatians to feel virtuous and have their good raw fun at the same time. They had a very real amount of it, too, until the Kefauver crime committee finally exposed Covington and Newport as The Syndicate's, the Mafia's gateway into Dixie.

Demara, feeling purged and spiritually cleansed since Punxsutawney, took one look at Newport, recognized it for what it is, and determined to stay there. The idea was not to enjoy the place but for the place to test him. One of his favorite and most intriguing examples of testing virtue was the practice of certain medieval monasteries to tempt their monks by inviting the most beautiful seductive young girls to share their cells with them. Those who survived the ordeal intact felt virtue had been heightened and resistance power strengthened. History does not record how those who succumbed felt.

We didn't stay to test the theory in Newport but got out of Newport and into the green, rolling pasture lands of the white-fenced horse country with its young colts, blue grass, old bourbon drinkers, whitewashed bricks, its evergreens, boxwood, Virginia creeper and English ivy, its courthouse squares faintly shadowed in early spring leaves giving an intimation of summer days ahead when the squares would be buried in shadows from a roof of fat green leaves, all of this which Kentuckians with good natural wisdom call their "pennyroyal."

"I think you'll be as moved as I have been when we get there," Demara said. "It isn't inconceivable that you might want to stay."

I pointed out to him again that I was a married man with children to fend for and that at the moment my religious bent, if I had one, was doing a good job hiding.

"There's no immunity from God," he said, in a rather unctuous way I thought. "There are many married men in monasteries. Look at the disciples."

I tried to change the conversation to something else because when Demara gets on religion, since he has spent so much time in various capacities in various religious orders, he tends to get overbearingly authoritative.

"When God calls, you come a runnin'," he said. "I'll tell you a little secret no one else knows. I went a runnin' to Gethsemani twice, once before the war as Anthony Ingolia and once after the war as Dr. French. No one ever noticed. They're so trusting. Oh, you're going to love it there."

While we headed in toward Bardstown, the market and tobacco center that dominates the area in which Gethsemani lies, he told me of his life among the Trappists. It was the first time he had ever volunteered information to me in detail and I felt I had taken the first step into the dark labyrinthian tangle of all his past lives.

There are possibly few more demanding lives that a man may choose to live than the life of a monk in the Order of Cistercians of the Strict Observance, the formal name for the order better known as Trappists.

Their day begins at two A.M. and it doesn't end until the sun has risen and gone down again and, in winter time, until the sun has been down a long time. It is a life of utter poverty, of heavy manual labor, endless charity, of disciplined intellectual study. It is also a life of vast rewards. The aim of these deprivations is not to tie or bind but to release the spirit from the bonds of the body and from temporal needs, and through this release to find a way to the more abundant life of the spirit.

There is joy to be found in this austerity, but the austerity is real enough. Although the monks operate a huge and successful modern model farm, the monks share in almost none of the fruits from it.

"I wilt to think of it," Demara said and I watched his tongue run over his lips.

They don't touch the meat they raise, or the eggs and even fish is forbidden. For most of the year the monk is deprived of the milk he takes from the cows he raises and worse, he eats little of the cheese the milk produces. This is especially painful since Gethsemani makes and sells one of the most brilliant Port de Salut type cheeses in the world. But very little of it passes the lips of the men who make it. To a man who loves cheese—and Demara is such a man—this is equal to putting an alcoholic in a winery and suggesting to him not to touch. If saints are still being made in this age, some of them are being fashioned in the cheese rooms at Gethsemani.

"Do you know," he told me, "I used to be jealous of sparrows? I'd see them eating the seeds of the grapes and I'd go home and dream about them. I'd see myself as a giant bird fluttering about in the vineyard eating seeds."

One of the offenses of Demara as a laybrother, in fact, was eating too many grapes out in the vineyards. "I felt like such a fraud, such a cheater out there," he explained to me later.

All of this can appear dreadful, even sadistic and masochistic to the outsider, but a glance at these men reassures one that to the dedicated monk these deprivations are only short cuts to the solitude and freedom he needs to reach his God.

Of all the hardships, however, one of them stands alone. For the life of the contemplative, almost complete and total silence is demanded. The unendurable loneliness to the not completely dedicated monk can be imagined. The toughest convicts, in fact, would crack under a few days of the routine of the gentle monks.

While he told me these things I could see Demara's hands begin to clench and unfold and clench again. He was reliving the terrible frustrations of trying to explain in sign language some vital piece of information; some subtle point, some light piece of brotherly information. It was so frustrating that Demara had an almost constant, barely controllable urge to one day climb up into the tower of the Abbey church and deliver a ringing speech to his fellow monks.

The picture of Demara in his monastic robes, the cowl of his habit surrounding his great head and his lips, God help us, sealed shut, was a very hard one for me to see. I think Demara sensed this and it annoyed him.

"I was a good, solid laybrother," he told me. "I expect you to believe that. I'll admit I had faults but I stuck it out longer than a lot of them."

There can be no question about it. A Trappist monastery is a place that brings a man almost at once down to the very rock-hard essentials of his life and character. For an impostor to endure the almost merciless taking away of personality and the relentless invasion of privacy, is no mean feat. There were, as he told me, ways around the silence if you couldn't bear it. One was to work with the animals out in the fields and to raise holy hell, if that is the proper term, with the beasts.

"In my case," he told me, "when it got too hard, I used to have imaginery debates and conferences with myself. Sometimes I used to use some of my old selves. I'd have Dr. French argue about theology with, say, Anthony Ingolia while I—me, the real me, Demara—would be the judge. Of course, I had an advantage over most of the others in this."

The debates at times would get so real that Demara would leap up in guilt, wondering if he had really just said aloud what he heard in his head or whether he had imagined saying it. If no one was looking at him reproachfully, he felt he was safe in assuming his lips had remained sealed.

"I'll assure you of one thing, though," he told me. "I always tried to keep the topic religious."

At Bardstown we turned off onto a rural highway and from that onto a winding country road which meandered through some poor, mean country. The farms, the few still operating, showed it. This was Kentucky hardscrabble country where no man can be expected to make a good living. We drove past several log cabins—several with no windows or merely openings covered with burlap bags, the gaps between the logs chinked with clay—each of them sporting television aerials. We passed one woman out in her concrete-hard bare yard boiling clothes in a huge iron pot as her ancestors must have done several hundred years before her.

"A scene out of history," I said. And then we saw the man of the house, home from the hills, slouching on a stool on the porch, his rifle at rest, his dogs napping around him, watching an afternoon give-away television show from a set inside the blackness of the cabin. NBC and CBS, situated ages and a thousand miles away, were making a bigger inroad among the people along that country road than the great monastery only a mile or two away. But, then, anyone who is going to try and pit the miracle of God against the miracle of the watching tube must be prepared for a long, and losing, battle.

We took a turn around a "knob," a little stubby hill topped with trees, and Gethsemani unfolded before us.

"There she lies," Demara cried. His face was flushed with excitement. "Ah, the great place. See that great silver flash in the sky? That's the spire of the church. Oh, and that other thing. That big mushroom sitting over the plain? That's the water tower. They lost a lot of potential saints building that thing."

"They probably made a few, too."

"Well put, well put," he said gleefully. I had never seen him so filled with bubbling, joyous enthusiasm.

"This is *the* place for us," he announced. "I don't care what plans you may have, Crichton. We're staying here for a few days, a few weeks."

"I have a baby coming any day you know."

"Do you think He would let it die if you were *here?*" I think he was in earnest.

I was immensely impressed by the well-tended, lush-looking fields around us. It was hardscrabble country but the Trappists had made it bloom, a trick of theirs for some 850 years.

We turned off the road and into an avenue of towering, arching trees which reached over to join each other like the nave in a great Gothic cathedral. There was a peace and a silence that was at once infectious. We drove very slowly down the aisle and near the end of it parked the car. There was no hill and if we stayed any length of time I had very weak hopes that the car would start up again. I could not very well see myself asking a group of hooded monks to give me a push.

At the end of the nave was a low, gray stone wall and the gatehouse which was guarded by a heavy wooden door. The impostor was close to trembling with suppressed excitement.

"Now let me handle this. I know the way to do this, you know," he whispered to me.

Over the door was a large, plainly lettered sign which read:

PAX INTRANTIBUS

Peace on those who enter.

"Pay attention to that," he said. "Relax. Let yourself feel the place." I told him that it was impossible to resist; one was infiltrated with the aura of peace and silence.

On the door was a little bell-rope and Demara pulled it. Within a short time a friendly, middle-aged monk came to the door and opened the upper half of it. He looked at us inquisitively and I studied him hard to see if there was any sign of recognition. I couldn't tell.

"Have you come to stay or have you come to visit?" he asked.

"Visit," I said.

"We'll probably stay," Demara assured the monk. He asked us to wait and went away.

"I'll do all the talking here," he said.

Although the contemplative's regular lot is silence there are several monks who are not bound to total silence. These are the brothers who must deal with the outside world. To the very devout this is considered a hindrance, not a treat, since talking comes between him and his God. Since the outside world represents certain temptation and possible corruption those who are to deal with the outside world are chosen by their brother monks as the men among them most capable of resisting the lures of the world. In other times these would be the men who might be martyrs. They might yet be.

The gatekeeper returned with a small, wiry-looking monk in a brown habit. It was impossible to tell if he were twenty-five or forty-five. He had about him a completely other-worldly innocence that suggested another age, even angels, so that we were both stunned when the monk, who was to be our guide, spoke in the accents of Brooklyn; not just Brooklynese of the middle classes but the back-alley accents of Red Hook and Greenpernt, spelled *point,* what in New York is known as a "hard-pavement kid."

"So whaddaya? Visitin' uh stayin'?" he asked.

"Visiting," I said.

"Staying," Demara said. The monk looked bewildered for the moment, I don't think he was accustomed to the sound of discord, but Demara slammed me with his elbow and announced again he would do the talking.

I won't attempt here to reproduce the monk's accent. It is not a dese, dem and dose affair at all but a much subtler, richer corruption of the language accomplished by dropping r's in the wrong places and putting them back in even worse places.

Looking at him, I wondered what his old street gang would make of him now, standing in the budding Guest Garden in a Trappist monastery, the brown cowl hiding the shyness and yet toughness of his face, preparing to introduce some of the highest refinements of the Church to two travelers come in off the road.

We talked for a moment about how much he missed Brooklyn; mostly he missed the smells—the asphalt bubbling in the streets on a hot July afternoon, the smell of oil freshly poured on the water at the Brooklyn Navy yard and the sounds of the streets, even the sounds of the people upstairs going after each other with malicious intent on a night when people take their blankets and go down to Coney Island to sleep on the beach. Then he turned and beckoned us to follow him.

We made a tour of the garden first during which he dutifully pointed out the garden's strange and unusual array of trees collected from all over the world, and as he did, I noticed Demara lagging behind us. Just as our guide began working the intricate lock on a gate door I saw Demara suddenly make a swift run for the fountain which stood in the middle of the garden. When the monk turned around to usher us out, there was Demara running his hands and arms around in the pool of water at the base of the fountain. For the second time the monk seemed deeply puzzled, the way a young child does who isn't afraid to profess ignorance.

"I have hot hands," Demara said, winking openly at me. "A strange disease. When the heat hits me, I have to cool them."

The monk accepted it completely. As we followed him across a large work area Demara explained what he had been doing. Years before, when he had first come to Gethsemani, in a gesture of riddance to the outside world, Demara had slid off his chain and army dogtags and, in a ceremonial gesture, sunk them in the pool. It occurred to me later that he was also destroying evidence. Even later it occurred to me, knowing Demara better, that he might also still have some use for those tags.

We were taken through the refectory and shown the very simple fare the monks would soon be eating; a bowl of vegetable soup, a plate of beans, a vegetable, a platter of brown bread and water—it was the big meal of the day —and then we passed through the monk's dormitory, the library and scriptorium and, finally, into the Chapter Room. The Chapter Room was in the monks' cloister and it is what might be called an organization room for the monks where lessons are given, where laybrothers get their first lessons in silence, where recalcitrant religieux like Demara confessed their errors at the Chapter of Faults. When we came in we startled several young monks who were deep in prayer and who chose to flee at the sight of the likes of us. As we went through corridors and in and out of buildings we passed a great many monks, many of whom must have been at Gethsemani when Demara had been there. None recognized him. I was surprised to see the number of smiling faces. In fact almost everyone was smiling all the time, destroying my image of the grim, gray monk.

It was in the Chapter Room that something startling happened. As our guide was hidden by his cowl, I had not realized how puzzled and anxious he had become. Whenever anything was pointed out to us, Demara would elaborate on the guide's answer. In the cheese rooms, when the guide had shown us the packaging section, it was Demara who gave the lecture on the now world-wide distribution of these famous cheeses.

"Is that right?" the guide said.

In describing the sight of several monks we had seen stop their work and sink into attitudes of contemplation, he was no match for Demara's fluency about the art.

"O Beato solitudo! O Sola Beatitudo!" Demara said.

"That's it in a nutshell," the guide agreed. "You've hit the nail on the head."

I could see that he was upset and bewildered.

"I'm going to leave you now," he said to us. "I'm going to get you someone who knows more than I do." With a nod and a shy, beatific smile he suddenly left the room, leaving us alone.

"He knows us," I said.

"He doesn't," Fred said easily. "I confounded him with my knowledge."

"You overdid it. You talked too much."

Demara favored me with a look of great wisdom.

"Do you think the man owns the *capacity* to suspicion people? It's beyond his experience. His nature is to believe."

We waited patiently and then restlessly for someone to come.

"I don't know why we have to wait, I can show you the place as well as anyone else," Demara said.

It was getting late in the afternoon. The sun was angling in at the windows, and, except where the sun was actually striking objects in the room, the room was filling up with gloom. We didn't notice the new Father when he came in through the door, and when he introduced himself, standing with his back to the light, he was almost invisible.

"Have you seen the abbey church yet?" he asked us. His voice in that large room was low, distant and hollow. I waited for Demara to answer but when he didn't I said no.

We were led, then, into the great solemn arched vault of the abbey church. At the sight of the old imposing place Demara, close by me, gave an involuntary gasp of recognition. We walked slowly down the church past the enormous choir stalls, deep, dark wooden stalls, high and polished by the backs of men who had leaned and touched the wood for a century. In front of each stall stood an enormous bound book of chants. Some of the books, easily a foot or more thick, bound in brass, must have weighed thirty or forty pounds.

"Oh, I was happy here," Demara sighed. "I was so happy here."

While our new guide went well ahead, Demara hefted one of the song books to show me the weight of it and then opened it to show me the painfully beautiful lettering of each page. Many of the books were ancient and priceless. It was clearly here that man's thirst for opulence and art had found an outlet. We went through the choir and up into the sanctuary where the priest stopped. When he lifted back the cowl of his robe we could see, in the steep silence of the great room, that he wore the tonsured hair of the monk, the hair halo that novitiates wear but most veterans soon give up as possibly appearing too obviously holy or beatific. Here again the light streaming in through the colored glass gave an ethereal, even eerie, tone to the hall.

"Have either of you ever been here before?" he asked. Again he had maneuvered himself in front of a shaft of light so that it was hard to make out his face, and his voice, hollow as voices will be in a chamber of that size, seemed disembodied. The question chilled me. I didn't feel it was my responsibility to answer for either of us.

"Have either of you ever been here before?" he asked again. The question seemed like an echo.

I looked to Demara to make an answer. He looked as bland and as cool as he had when he answered the other monk's question.

"I asked," he said, not unkindly, "if either of you have ever been here before."

I felt an answer could not wait.

"No," I said. "But I used to go to a somewhat monastic school," I felt I had to add.

"Oh?"

"But it wasn't like this. Benedictines."

"Oh."

"English Benedictines. Not like this. They had it easy."

"Oh," he said. Each time the voice sounded a bit more disembodied and I felt I had to explain more.

"It was in Rhode Island. A fine place."

"But not like this," he said. "And you?" he said to Demara. Demara simply looked right through the monk. "Come," he finally said.

We followed our guide through a maze of halls and rooms which I can't now recall. Somewhere a bell began tolling faintly and somewhere else, somewhat stronger, the deep solemn sweet sound of men's voices singing in the modal scale reached us. When we reached a new, rather modern-looking building, we stopped. The doors of the building were large and made of a striking kind of wood, and the walls were made of poured concrete, unusual for the abbey. Over the entrance were carved the dates 1098 and 1849, the year the order was founded and the year Gethsemani was founded. Beneath it was the simple legend:

GOD ALONE

Our guide was evidently proud of the building since we

looked at it in silence for what seemed to me to be an excessive time, until he turned back to us and then turned directly to Demara.

"This is new since you were here," he said.

I could not bring myself to turn and look at Demara. I heard a sucking in of wind as if he had been struck.

"He knows," he said, in a hoarse whisper.

I went across to him and was astonished to find that his face was a glowing red. He was burning with embarrassment—or was it shame.

"He knows," he said with a sob. Even in the gloom of the big room I could see that tears had started up in his eyes and one or two already were falling. He turned on his heel and he began moving.

As I started to follow him, I doubted if he knew where he was going. It was simply vital for him to be moving and to get out. For a big man he can move with surprising stealth and speed, much like a bear. We went out one door and found ourselves in an old primitive graveyard. It was one which Demara only a few minutes before had told me he had always wanted to be buried in. From the graveyard we came back into the Gethsemani buildings and I found myself rushing past lines of staring and startled monks and laybrothers, and then we were outdoors once again, running across the Guest Garden, in through the gatehouse and out onto the tree-arched lane where the Death Wagon waited for us.

I have always admired Demara's ability to keep control of things even when they seem to be falling apart. Despite the shame he was experiencing and despite the tears coursing down his florid face, as we ran through the gate he called back to me:

"They ought to turn that sign around."

I looked up as I ran under it. *Pax Intrantibus.*

"They don't need it. It's the ones going out who need it."

When we got to the car it started up at once, and I felt thankful for that small favor.

"Where to?" I asked. I felt that since he had made his joke that his fund of good humor was being restored. He didn't answer. When I looked over at him I was stunned by his appearance. The tears were gone and the redness was gone and his face was white and puffy and sunk in upon itself.

"Don't you look at me," he cried.

He opened the right front compartment of the dash-board, and he took out a pint of Kentucky bourbon and twisted the cap off with a furious jerk of his thumb and forefinger. He put the bottle to his lips, tilted his head back and poured perhaps one-fourth of the pint down his throat before he pulled the bottle away.

"He knew," he said violently. "They all knew. I can hear them laughing. The day they got even with the great impostor. But I know something they don't know." He patted the bottle. "I know a way to forget."

When I looked back at him again, the bottle was nearly empty and his face was as black as thunderheads before a heat storm.

10.

The days that followed Gethsemani were hard ones. I don't know where the impostor got his liquor; I never actually saw him buy it, and I don't know how he drank it all, although I watched him do it. I know how he paid for it, because by that time I was paying for it. The days, the wild days, stay with me now mainly as a mixture of odd flashes of disconnected memory, sudden rare quick glimpses into the mind of Demara, times of sadness and personal abuse and trouble.

The drinking began in earnest the morning after we fled from Gethsemani. I woke up, I suppose it was six in the morning, and looked down over the edge of the double-decked bunk. We were in central rural Tennessee in a motel mainly designed for truckers. With some disbelief in what I was seeing, and with some horror, I watched Demara begin mixing a pre-breakfast, dry martini in a water tumbler.

By the time breakfast came, the bottle of gin, a good bottle of Gordon's I had been shepherding since Erie, was almost gone. The impostor wasn't, however. He seemed completely sober. After breakfast he opened a quart of ginger ale, poured out half of it, in cavalier fashion, and poured in a pint of whisky. At lunch time this brew was gone. In the afternoon the process was repeated and before and after dinner a bottle of Early Times was consumed. The last I saw of my man that day, he was sitting down on his bed uncorking the first of a case of beer, preparing to re-read *True Tales from the Annals of Crime and Rascality.*

In the morning he was up before I was, shaved, in reasonably good spirits, and I watched as he downed the last four bottles of beer to work up an appetite for breakfast.

The trying thing to me was that I couldn't tell when he was drunk or not. All I was certain of was that he was trying his best to get drunk and drown the painful thoughts of what had happened to him at Gethsemani. There were no lapses of memory, no real moments of violence and no drunken behavior such as staggering around town squares and receiving the disapproving stares of the Southern Baptists. Through it all, in fact, he seemed to act with the rather exaggerated grace of a courtly Victorian grandfather. Perhaps he was just trying to keep a grip on himself. Except for an occasional look of utter despair, he was charming to all the world except to me. The odor of whisky followed him around a room like an invisible cloak, but this didn't seem to bother anyone.

"Charming," people said. "Just charming." The fake, I thought.

"Why can't you treat me with a little of that charm?" I finally asked him.

"Oh, you," he said. "That's the price *you* have to pay for knowing the real Demara. You won't be satisfied with the false one so you get the real one. Don't like it, eh?"

I telephoned home and spoke to a doctor I had known a long time and who had a great deal of experience dealing with drinking patients.

"Oh, no," he assured me. "He isn't drinking that much. He couldn't be."

Not only was I watching him drink that much, I was beginning to have to pay for it. I was sure of his capacity.

"I think he's trying to trick you," the doctor finally said.

"Oh, he wouldn't do *that*," I said.

"You can never tell," the doctor said.

No hope there. I suspect it was the drinking, but it was hard to tell. Most people who get hostile while drinking soon tend to get into violent scrapes or fall on their heads, but with Demara things were never that simple. I could never tell whether the alcohol was speaking for him or if it only provided an excuse for the real Demara to come out and lambaste me. An armed truce, a controlled suspicious hostility broke out between us. Neither would admit we were annoyed or mad at the other, but we sat and watched and waited for the other to make a false move.

"Thinking of leaving me?" Demara asked one afternoon. "Go ahead. I'd welcome it. I'll sue you for a breach of contract that would ruin you. Imagine what Random House would say about you." He poured himself a long drink. "You're latched on to the tar baby, buddy, and you are *stuck*."

Through all of it one thing sustained me. Despite all the nonsense and abuse, I was being rewarded with increasingly revealing peeks into the real man through cracks opened by one-hundred-proof bourbon. For example, one thing that had always puzzled me was how Demara had been able to fool fellow faculty members. It is one thing to stay a day or two ahead of the students, but it is another to cover ignorance in a two-hour faculty lunch.

"Never win an argument," he told me.

It is Demara's feeling that it is easier to conceal ignorance than it is to acquire knowledge, and a little later Demara dramatized for me his "never win an argument" approach.

Imagine a situation where someone challenges one of Demara's many areas of no-knowledge.

"Why, Descartes never made any such statement," his challenger says.

"He didn't? Well, what's your version, Doctor?" Demara says.

As the professor explains his theories on the philosophy of Descartes, Demara assumes the look of an enraptured child hearing the *Three Bears* for the first time. When the doctor is through Demara says:

"I never really thought of it that way before. Would you mind very much if I made a few notes?"

Does the professor think that Demara is stupid, or ill-informed? Does he object to a fellow teacher taking notes on his wisdom?

He does not! He thinks that Demara is the very first professor he has ever met with an open, honest, enquiring mind, who is capable of understanding and appreciating the truth; the truth as revealed by the professor, of course.

It is a brilliant, simple human truth. I asked him why he never tried it on me.

"As long as you have that orange notebook, you don't win anything from me," he said.

I also finally resolved to my satisfaction whether Demara, as many people suspect, is a genius or not. He is not. He is a prodigious reader, he is, in the terms of the theater, a "quick study" who can grasp things with unusual and, at times, amazing rapidity, but his genius is really a disguise for a simple, but brilliant, grasp of human nature and human weaknesses. He *knows* people and he knows how to utilize what he knows about them. Some demagogues know this, good politicians and good priests know this, and theater people often have this grasp of people as a group.

But one of Demara's graces is that he is not cynical about his knowledge or talent. Beneath it all, what makes this knowledge work is that he really loves people and people really love him.

I found another thing, a truth that infuriates him when I mention it. He is a hopeless romantic. To Demara, the disaster of growing up is the loss of innocence. After that comes the loss of a man's dream and finally the loss of hope. But the first is the loss of innocence. It is a Demara contention that the greatest tragedy in the lives of many Americans is their discovery that Santa Claus is not real; a setback from which many never recover.

My own feeling about Demara is that one of the compulsions that drives him along the path he takes is a simple romantic urge to find some world or niche where innocence has not been lost or where it might be regained again.

He hasn't found it, and, although he increasingly doubts that he is going to find such a world, sooner or later some new frontier always summons him.

"Oh, yes, I still have hope," he said to me. "But it is fading, fading, fading. Pass me that bottle opener, please."

Deep down Demara has a dislike and even a distrust of intellectuals, educators, artists and what have become to be known as "other-directed" types, people who acquire or learn their values rather than have them stubbornly rooted in their own being. The reason for this is that he can almost always fool or bluff the intellectuals; the farmers give him a much harder time of it. This makes Demara feel the thinkers are phonies and so he can't abide them.

He *hates* phonies.

One reason he has so few qualms about some of his hoaxes is that he doesn't feel qualms are called for. Demara is fond of quoting Yellow Kid Weil, an old champion con man. Weil says: "I never cheated an honest man, only rascals. They may have been respectable, but they were never any good. They wanted something for nothing. I gave them nothing for something."

This, Demara feels, applies to many of the colleges and institutions who hired him.

"They didn't hire me, the man. They didn't care about me, the man. They wanted the record, the title, the degrees. How the world loves a Ph.D! I gave it to them; they took it. But let's not have any tears, on either side."

Behind it all I was still waiting for the very ripe moment when I could ask Demara just when it was and how it was that he got the outlandish summoning of nerve to take scalpel in hand and, on the high seas in Korea, begin moving it down the length of a human body. Everytime I got close, he turned on me like a bear.

"You don't dare ask that," he would growl. "You and that goddamn notebook. You're just dying to put the answer in there."

Along about the eighth day, the drinking began to have a visible effect. For the first time he began to slur words and look physically racked. He began to have a series of little fantasies. One concerned his television future.

He became obsessed with the idea that he could be the greatest bargain guest "This Is Your Life" ever had. The program could be called These Were Your Lives and run for twenty-eight straight weeks. This would save a fortune in transportation for guests, for one thing. He also had an idea that he might be available to appear on "What's My Line" for a half-year running.

In a roadhouse across the Mississippi River in Arkansas he finally created a scene. The place had been emptied of a group of ladies on their way to some religious to-do and Demara felt terribly depressed. He began singing an old rescue mission song.

> *"Throw out the life line across the dark wave*
> *There is a brother someone should save*

Throw out the life line
Throw out the life line
Someone is sinking today."

They threw us out.

That night, on that eighth day, he finally became drunk. He had switched to rum, a habit he had picked up in the Royal Canadian Navy when he was made officer in charge of administering the daily rum ration, a high honor. His choice these days was Demerara rum, a powerful, rich, heavy-bodied rum from British Guiana, perhaps because of the similarity of names, but more likely because of the blazing punch it contained. Demara was downing it, mixing it half and half in Coca-Cola quarts, which seemed to me a desperate thing to do.

That night, slumping on the edge of his motel bed, he surprised me by suddenly announcing that he was a monstrous wretch.

"I don't know how you've suffered me." He handed me his beloved bottle of rum. "Here, you need this more than me."

It went down nicely until it began to flame in my stomach.

"Don't smoke," he warned. He went across to a warped tin mirror, which didn't help matters.

"Look at me, a red-faced pudding, puffed to the gills with rum. What a pudding-filled disgrace." He poured himself another tumbler of rum. "Don't worry about this," he said to me. "This is going to stop now." He looked in the mirror again.

"A man of quality with no qualities. A man of talent with no talent. A man of faith with nothing to believe in." He turned on me. "Did you ever hear a definition of Hell? You just did."

He went to the door and assumed a theatric pose.

"Wherein is he good but to taste sack and drink it?
Wherein crafty but in villainy.
Wherein villainous but in all things?
Wherein worthy but in nothing."

He turned back into the room. "Oh, goddamn it, I'm going to start crying." I discreetly started out the door. "Don't leave me," he said, but I went and pretended to work on the car. It was going to be terrible if it was going to get any worse than it was. About an hour later he came to the door and told me it was all right now, that I could come in. Demara has astonishing recuperative powers. He did, indeed, look fine.

"Oh, and in the back of the car, underneath the tires, you'll find an emergency jug of California's sunniest wine. Be a good boy and bring in the sunshine, will you?" He saw me hesitate. "Don't worry. This means the end."

I believed him. Inside he asked me to sit down, put my feet up on the bed, open my notebook, open the wine, that he had some things he wanted to tell me.

For the next four hours, while I wrote but finally only listened, as he drank well into the gallon of wine and slumped lower and lower, he began revealing the secrets of his past. He told me of his abortive love affair while in the Canadian Navy and he told me of the first operations.

It was then a matter of desperation that did it; if he didn't cut, the sailors died. He told me of the Texas prison days and of the people who had helped him when they shouldn't and others who had let him down to save themselves from scandal. He told me that night at least ten lives he had led for brief times that I had no inkling of. For the first time he told me about the early days in Lawrence, and he talked about his mother and father, both of whom had lived through most of his escapades. At times he withdrew into a deep, physically sick remorse and then he would blossom into a jovial flowering of memory. He was staging a magnificent performance, sinking into depths, rising back up out of the mire he had put himself in—at times loud and at others low and confiding.

It was both intriguing and exhausting. How much of it could I believe? But at last I could recognize that the midnight orgy of self-revelation was over.

"Now, a final confession. In the back of the car there's one last bottle of wine." By now I was fairly drunk myself and when I returned with the bottle he seemed mightily pleased. This was a great wine, a good, stout Burgundy he must have carried all the way from New York.

"One last peep show," he said, holding the bottle up to the light. He told me how when he was a novitiate in various religious orders he used to make it a practice to drink a quart of whisky in front of fellow religieux, shocking them by the performance. The reasoning was astute. Ever after that he would pile up points for good behavior simply by not being drunk. He recited what I later learned is *The Jolly Priest's Confession,* which was written in 1180. The poem usually accompanied his drinking bouts.

"Ah, I was such a scandalous boy," he said, and began reciting:

> *"Die I must, but let me die drinking in an inn!*
> *Hold the wine glass to my lips sparkling from the bin*
> *So, when angels flutter down to take me from my sin*
> *'Ah, God have mercy on this sot' the cherubs will*
> *   begin."*

He drained a good part of the Burgundy in one gargantuan, Rabelaisian pull and then he waddled across the room and fell face forward on his bed, and ceased to move.

I sat for a few moments wondering at him. The Burgundy was nearly drained; the imposter was drained. It would take a lot to fill him again and my hope then was that he was not going to remember much, if any, of what he had said this night. I fingered the bottle and took a last ceremonial sip myself and then emptied on the earth outside, fittingly I felt, the last good redness of the wine.

I had just gotten into my own bed when a car drove up, the lights splayed into the room and then I heard a woman's high heels clack up the stairs of the bungalow next to ours.

"What did you do, just sit there all night?" she said. Her voice pierced through the walls of our cabin. "Weren't you bored?"

"No," a man said softly, in a voice I could hear as clearly as if he had been sitting at the edge of my bed. "I

wasn't bored. Fact is, it was just about the most interesting night I ever spent in my life."

He had heard it all.

The chance that Demara was now snoring away, un-
aware that he had been broadcasting to strangers the
most intimate secrets of his life, I consider a true blessing. Later I sneaked out to see where the car was from. It
bore Michigan plates, was bought in Battle Creek, and I
can only assume that somewhere in Battle Creek there
lives a quiet man who knows more about the secret life
of the great impostor than anyone else on earth except for
Demara and myself and, if his memory is better than
mine, more than me.

In the morning he woke me demanding to know where
the last of the wine had gone. I felt sick when I heard his
angry voice; I had entertained the hope that Demara had
at last been purged. But then he broke into a smile and it
was as if the sun had come out again after a week of fog
and rain. At breakfast I watched him studying my face
in the chrome of the coffee urn in front of us.

"Pretty crazy conversation last night, huh?" he asked
casually.

"Pretty boring," I said glumly. I took a chance that he
didn't remember, and I made up a rather fantastic story
about how all night Demara had buried me with tales of
how he had once played professional football under the
name of Bull Jones.

"I told you that?" he asked, in a delighted voice. "That
I played for the Chicago Bears?"

"You detailed every play of the 1948 season," I said, and he let out a roar of laughter.

"Oh, that was *foxy* of me. Was that ever *foxy* of me. And here I was thinking I had spent the night spilling my guts out to you."

"Foxy," I said, pretending to be deeply hurt and angry. "You're nothing but a low-down, dirty liar." The counterman turned on us, getting set for a showdown. Southerners are touchy that way. He was astonished to see Demara break out in a beatific smile.

"Isn't that just the truth?" he said sweetly. "Don't worry, little busy writer," he said, patting me on the back, "Big Daddy tell you some secrets by'n by."

That was the turning point for me. From that time on, whole areas of his past, that Demara didn't realize I knew about, took on new shapes and importance for me as he mentioned names or incidents which he felt he was disguising but which I now recognized. For once I had a secret advantage over the impostor; I had a little key that let me into rooms I shouldn't have been prowling in.

11.

The dark drinking days were over and there came a time of rambling. The trouble lay with Texas. We went into Arkansas and I found we couldn't get out again. Demara had never been punished for his posing as a warden in the Texas prison system and over the years he had arrived at a conviction, amounting to a fatal obsession, that somehow or other before his life was done he was going to have to pay for what he had done.

"They're going to get me. Make no mistake about that," he assured me. He was convinced that every trooper in Texas carried an open warrant for his arrest should he ever sully Texas soil again. "I just want to feel right and ready for it when it comes."

"Fred, you don't *have* to go," I would say.

"I've got a debt to pay," he would answer sadly, "and I always pay my debts."

The result was that every time the car headed in the direction of Texas, Demara would appear to collapse. I was terrified that the tension might turn him back to the bottle. For just my own sake I couldn't let that happen again. So we drove about the fringes of Texas, fiddling

our way through Arkansas, pretending to each other that
the border didn't lie just beyond the next cotton field or
stand of pine.

It wasn't all lost time, however, since we visited New
Subiaco Abbey in the Ozarks, a Benedictine monastery far
up in the hills, where Demara had served as a science instructor. And then there was an afternoon in the rice
country of southeastern Arkansas that perhaps will go
down in history as an example of the worst meal yet served
in the history of the states. I know this is a big claim for a
big country, but I can only record what happened to us.

The rice lands had faded from view and we were traveling through a low-lying swamp—the kind of place in the
rural South that is always known as Someone's Dismals—
when we came upon what we both felt was an apparition.
Snug among the moss-draped oaks, hard by a stand of
floating cypress, was a shining, chrome-plated highway
diner and Bar-B-Q.

"It looks clean," Demara said.

"It looks good." We both agreed that anyone making a
success of running a restaurant in Someone's Dismals
must serve excellent food.

"This is the place for us," we both agreed.

The restaurant was a tribute to the New South. Not
too long ago it was man's fate in small southern towns to
have to eat in non-air conditioned, little, slopy-roof eating
places that usually had on the menu just what everyone
else in town had on their menu that night—some smoked
country ham, platters of black-eyed peas cooked in ham
hocks, fresh country greens from the garden, such as
turnip tops and collards, a pitcher of buttermilk, clabber

biscuits hot with mayhaw jelly—the kind of meal that couldn't be duplicated anywhere else in the world and which called for a two-hour nap after eating.

Today, thanks to the new prosperity of the New South, you can't find these places any more except perhaps for Negro restaurants, but then whites are forbidden to go there. I have often wondered if they have a carry-out service. Today what you can find, beyond the penetration of Howard Johnson, is eleven thousand new, shiny, roadside diners, every one of which looks and smells like the highway leading into Kenosha, Wisconsin. In this at least, the South has surrendered. When we went inside, if it hadn't been for the sphagnum moss sweeping in the wind outside, I could not have told we were deep in the dells of Arkansas.

The owner of the place was another tribute to the New South; anxious and eager, peppy and utterly dying to please. This once unreconstructed rebel now had a subscription to *Better Homes and Gardens* and read every word of it. When we sat down on the stainless steel chairs, he handed us a menu pressed in plastic.

"Order the chicken," Demara advised. "They really know how to cook it down in these swamps. Birds feed on wild rice. Knock your eye out."

"You just bet your life," our host sang out. "Chicken it is," and he almost danced his way to the freezer in the corner. Demara was not able to view the proceedings the way I was, his back being to the counter, and I was just as happy about that. When he is very hungry, which he was, he has a way of sitting stock-still, studying his hands, a testament to monumental patience, until his food arrives.

It was with a certain feeling of misgiving that I watched our chef open the door of the giant-size freezing unit and retrieve from inside a long, skinny, neatly packaged in plastic, fowl. From where I sat I could see that it came from Illinois.

The bird clearly had the consistency of tungsten. To make it pliable the chef cracked it once on his stainless steel work table, causing Demara to lurch, and then he pitched it into a large, electric deep-fat fryer.

"Mashtafrod?" he called.

"Mashed," Demara said.

"Same here," I said.

He opened the door of the freezer again and he took out this time a plastic bag filled with pre-frozen mashed potatoes. He slammed these down onto the table also but they didn't make nearly the sound the chicken had and then he simply dumped them in their bag into a boiling urn of coffee. That is efficiency, I noticed, and hoped there wasn't a pin size hole in the bag.

"Peezeacarts?" he called again.

"Carrots," Demara said. I said I'd take the same. The freezer opened again and he took out a petrified bunch of carrots in a plastic bag. He knifed open the bag and popped the carrots into the deep-fat fryer. He must have seen the look on my face.

"New Southern style," he said. "Efficiency."

"Ah," I nodded approvingly. "The new way."

"That *is* the ticket," he said. "Everythang up and boomin' in Dixie today."

"What's he doing?" Demara said.

"He just popped the carrots in," I told him.

"Good," he said. "Good."

The coffee was beginning to bubble against the top of the urn and I could hear the potatoes tinkling against the lid. At the sound he whipped off the top and retrieved the bag with the aid of a little trout net.

"So that's the way you do it," I marveled.

"That's the way we do thangs *these* days," he said proudly.

"What's he doing now?" Demara said.

"Potatoes are accounted for," I said.

"Good," he said. "Good!"

I felt like someone left over from a by-passed era. To while away an idle moment our host played some rock 'n' roll religious numbers on the juke box, good songs really, all about being nice to Jesus and then getting your girl back, and a bell rang.

"There's the carts," he sang out. I watched him pull them out of the deep fat fryer with a pair of obstetrical tongs.

"You give me the tools," he chuckled, "and I will do the job. That's all we need down here."

Another bell rang. "There's your 'taters," he called. He trotted to a new pot of water I hadn't noticed, a cleansing pot of some kind, and swooped the bag out with his net.

"What now?"

"He's got the spuds again," I told Demara.

"Not again," he groaned.

Then a loud bell, it was a buzzer really, sounded.

"And there's the chicken," the chef cried.

I noticed that he could not seem to get his carving fork

into the flank of the bird to pull it out of the bubbling fat, and after a few tries he got his forceps again.

"Hurry," Demara suddenly shouted. "I am starving."

"You're gonna' be glad you waited, mister," the chef assured him.

It was too big and slick for the forceps. When he felt that neither of us was looking, I saw him run his hand into the fryer at the risk of broiling his hand. He yanked the bird, sharp, quick, and it came out all right, but it got loose and flew along behind the counter until it skidded to a stop on the duck boards that covered the floor.

"What's he doing?" Demara said. I had to admit I didn't know. When Demara turned to look at the man he wasn't in sight. I knew what he was doing, of course, down on his hands and knees trying to get the chicken back up on the steel table. When he came up he wore a big, re-assuring smile and it placated Demara. He finally got it up by a piece of trickery. With a string he roped the thing about one leg and then, moving quietly, he hauled it up onto the table as if pulling a bucket of water out of a narrow well. Then he began to carve.

The noise was enough to cause Demara to swivel around again.

"Never saw anyone carve a chicken with a meat cleaver before," he said. "That's the beauty of traveling; you learn all sorts of things. These country boys know their business and don't you think they don't."

Demara didn't see him using the same cleaver on the mashed potatoes but when it was all assembled I will be the first to admit that it looked good on the plate. Demara rubbed his hands in anticipation.

"He took his time, but it was worth it," he said to me, with a jolly wink.

The outsides of the food were all done. Since they had been buried and drenched in hog fat they were, as a matter of fact, a little scorched. Inside, however, on my plate at least, no such damage had been done. Nothing had been done.

It was sad to watch the impostor begin to go at his chicken, since he is a man who likes his food. It was not possible for him to shave a single sliver from the fowl's flank.

"Tell him to get me another knife," Demara said, hopefully.

"Another knife, please."

"You just bet your life," he said, and he gave me a formidable looking thing which I passed to Demara. I felt I already had bet my life. It was a futile move anyway. Even had the knife worked Demara was still only armed with the same set of teeth.

"Don't give me looks like that," I said.

"You're the one who said it looked good," he grumbled. Demara can be extraordinarily generous at times.

"Ah, well, all right," he said with true magnanimity, "we will be vegetarians." He skipped the carrots because they did not, in truth, look quite all right and he pitched into his potatoes. I had already surrendered on them and was over at a candy counter looking at packages of crackers I might buy, when I heard his cry.

"Lord help me," he shouted. "There are ice cubes in my potatoes."

From a gourmet, I have never heard a sadder cry. He got up from his seat and began moving toward the door, seeming to be immersed in shock. Our host was still smiling broadly from behind his counter.

"Take that idiotic look off your face," Demara shouted. "Your people are dying!"

He reached the door and he turned back again.

"You have just set a record," Demara called. "A world's record. I am a man who can eat *anything:* I can eat *nothing.*"

He went out of the door, marching in a military manner which he must have learned in the Royal Canadian Navy. He looked to me as if he were going to come to parade rest before a firing squad, but then he came back in through the screen door again.

"May you die of stomach rot from eating your own food."

The man looked very sad.

"Sort of a sorehead, isn't he?" he said to me.

"He is kind of particular about his food. He's French, you know." I felt like a traitor, but then I hate a scene. I decided that I would stay behind at least a moment and slip the man a dollar to cover his time and labor, when Demara came in and caught me.

"Oh, no you don't," he shouted at me. "Take that money back. That man tried to kill me."

When we got into the car the chef, a man of unbounded optimism, came to the screen door and called "Come back soon again, h'year?" I tried to persuade Demara to stay in the car but he had to get out again.

"The day I come back I'm coming with a gun," Demara called to him. "Not to shoot you but to shoot myself. Because that's the day I'll know I've gone mad."

We drove through the swampy sadness of Somebody's Dismals and I knew we never would be back.

In Paragould, Arkansas, late in the evening, Demara asked to take the wheel and told me to get in the back and take a nap, that he would wake me when we got where he wanted to go.

When he woke me a few hours later he asked me to see if I noticed anything different. For a long time I didn't see anything especially changed, and then I began to notice that the license plates all read *Land of Lincoln*.

This was madness. It simply could not be. We were in Illinois. I suddenly figured with a mixture of anger and fear that Demara had drugged me in some fashion.

He hadn't. Demara is an acute student of regional geography, as befits his profession. Since he has been so many people, he has had to acquire a sound knowledge of many diverse regions. But he is amazingly clever about this. He never learns too much, for this reason. The usual impostor, to make himself believable, cuts out a silhouette of the person he wants to be and then begins piling mound after mound of information behind the silhouette to give it shape. As soon as he meets someone from the town or region he is supposed to come from, to convince that person he really is from there, he overwhelms him with "convincing" detail. What he doesn't realize is that this makes him increasingly vulnerable; the more he knows, the more he must know.

Demara tries never to say anything but lets the other person do the talking. If he is asked, "Then you must have gone to P.S. 8," he says, "No, I went away to school." He has never been trapped because of his geography, but he knows regional geography, if only to facilitate an occasional escape route.

We were in southern Illinois, "down in Egypt land" as they say. Cairo, Illinois, is almost 250 miles south of Mark Twain's sleepy, southern river town of Hannibal. It is only a long whoop and holler to darkest Mississippi and, incredibly enough, Cairo, Illinois, is closer on the fly to Texas than to Chicago.

It bemused him to be there. And once there, despite the fact that we were closer to Texas than to Chicago, it was only natural we should go to the big city once in Illinois. Besides, several years before, on the run from that city, he had been forced to abandon an invaluable cache of credentials and personal records in a YMCA. He was determined to make an effort to get them back. "There's too many lives bundled up in that bag," he said.

We drove around the city revisiting the Clerics of St. Viator and looking at De Paul University, where Demara had been lured into taking six graduate courses in theology and in which he confounded everyone by amassing straight A's, and then went to a large YMCA on Indiana Avenue. They assured us they would have a record of a bag left there several years ago but not claimed.

"All right. Fine," Demara said. "I want to put a tracer

on a bag left here two years ago by me, Dr. Robert L. French."

There was no record of a bag being left under that name.

"Wait a minute. Try Dr. Cecil Boyce Hamann." The clerk eyed us suspiciously but dutifully flipped through his files.

"Oh God." Demara paused for what I felt was a conspicuously long time. "I've got it. Try Jones. Ben W. Jones," he said.

There were several Joneses but no Ben W.

"Arthur Moreland? How about that? Moreland," he asked, eagerly. The clerk shook his head. A look of anger crossed Demara's face.

"You're supposed to be the big expert around here," he said to me. "Come on. Who the hell *was* I two years ago?"

I didn't know, and I suggested he try just plain old Fred W. Demara. The impostor fixed me with a look filled with disgust.

"What would a bum like Demara be doing in a nice place like this?" he asked me.

I suddenly felt saddened for this man, standing angrily in the middle of a busy hotel, his face troubled and perplexed, trying to recall his own identity.

"Who the hell was I?" he said in despair and turned away.

I knew that things like that were increasingly coming to plague his over-peopled memory.

"Ghosts," he said, as he passed by me for the door. "My God, the ghosts. Ghosts, ghosts, ghosts."

I've not seen him sadder.

It was in Chicago, however, that Demara felt he had found the courage or the style to face Texas. He was not joyous about this but resigned to what must be. When he found it, he wanted to go at once. It was nighttime but we got back into the Death Wagon and went. My time sense is confused and so is my geographical sense. I think we flew by night by instinct and desire.

It was dark along the road when an incredible thing happened. Occasionally the hold of night was briefly broken by the flicker of light from some lonely rural cabin, but otherwise there was only the sense of blackness swishing by us until we saw ahead a splash of neon corrupting the country night.

"Restaurant," I said. "Want to risk it?"

"It looks clean enough, anyway," Demara said. When I parked I sensed that I was reliving a segment of some nightmare from the past, and I was just getting out of the car after Demara when I heard him running back toward me.

"Go *back*," he cried. "Go back."

"What is it? What is it?" I called to him. I felt he might have stumbled onto some country gang of robbers waiting for tourists in the night.

"It's the same place," he cried. "Keep the motor running."

A flash of light flooded out from behind him.

"I just *knew* you boys would be back," I heard his voice.

"The place with the ice cubes in the potatoes," Demara shouted.

The car wouldn't start, and, in what might be one of

Demara's worst moments, I had to ask the owner for a push.

"Not one thang too good for a regular customer," he said.

When the motor caught he pulled up alongside us.

"Next time I want you boys to come in and try the frozen cat fish, h'year?"

The thought caused me to shudder but Demara, more a gourmet, was deeply offended. He let out a shriek of genuine anguish, a cry of outraged sensibilities, that carried well across the stagnant water of the moss-draped dismals. I know that the people who lived out there think they heard the death cry of a loon that night.

"Well, what the hell," I said, when we were safely away. "It is optimism like that that helped to make America great."

He stared into the bleakness of the swamp.

"It sure as hell wasn't the food," he said bleakly.

We drove until we came to a town which now survives in my notes as G. B'you, Elev. 2, Pop. 109. It was a bayou-country crossroads: one gas station, a country store covered from the roof to the ground with Dr. Pepper and snuff ads and, surprisingly, an eating place. When we went inside we were astonished to see what must have been at least half of the region's population lined up along the walls. I felt we had intruded on a burial party.

"I don't think we should intrude," I whispered but, after his fashion, he barged in on the wake. We took one of the few tables.

"Oh, we're not serving now, it's after six o'clock," a waitress said.

"What's all this then," Demara demanded, scanning the line of long, sad faces.

"This here's the square dance." Noting the looks on our faces she added: "Hit's not steppin' off so smart."

I didn't know much about square dances, only having attended church dances back east, but it certainly was not stepping off smart. Most church square dances around New York are run to prove to people that they don't need drinks in order to get along with each other, but I have found that there is nothing like an old-fashioned square dance to get a man lusting after another man's wife. With cocktails one feels sort of sinister and only the wicked succumb, but at a square dance very hearty types can wind up rolling in the hay. I seriously recommend alcohol as the safer course in social Christian communication. But this one, under any guise, was not moving.

Five or six times while we sat there, the young man who was ostensibly the leader called out a dance, and his country band whipped up the tune but no one in the room found the courage or inspiration to move. Instead of going ahead with the number the leader would admit defeat. Three minutes later he would try again, each time with less assurance and less command.

"This is ridiculous," Demara announced.

With a sinking sensation, I watched Demara rise. He started along the rows of silent, even sullen, people, winking and smiling and nodding at them as he went, until he reached the home-brew public-address system the young country singers had rigged up.

"Howdy," he boomed to the leader. "Mind if I use this thing a minute?" His voice had a resonance that I hadn't heard since New York.

"No, sir," the leader said. He handed Demara the microphone as if it were a venomous reptile.

While the whole room eyed him carefully, guardedly, he took all the time he needed to adjust the mike, arrange the sound, do a testing routine and, in general, get every eye fixed on him.

"All right, folks," he bellowed in such a commanding way I found myself sitting bolt upright to attention. "Everyone on his feet, we're going to have a ball. You over there. Yes. You. And you, that big tall clunk over there." Everyone chuckled. It was me. "You too good to dance with *people*." Another laugh, a little warmer this time. "Old and young. Young and old. Don't go sneaking off over there. Everybody now. One. Two. Three. *On your feet.*"

I looked around the hall. Only one person was still sitting.

"What's the matter with you?" Demara demanded. There was a hush in the room.

"Ol' Cliff's got a bad leg."

"Bad leg?" Demara said. "What's so wrong with a bad leg. Supposing I told you people that I have a bad leg. Got it shot off in Korea. But don't you think I mean to dance all night until the sun comes up?"

Ol' Cliff grinned self-consciously and finally rose. He could hobble about quite well and actually his real trouble seemed to stem from a snootful of bayou moonshine. Once he stopped swaying, however, even Cliff seemed ready to ramble.

"Play something right now," Demara ordered. "Good and fast and loud."

The boy obliged. He was a good caller and he had the high, clean, snort-like sounds of a professional Mississippi hog caller. He simply lacked leadership. Under the master's wing, the boy blossomed. G. B'you began to jump.

After the first dance Demara began calling out for all the teen-age boys to dance with all the grandmothers, and when the giggling and whooping and hollering died down he turned the combination around. He kept the dances short and fast and he mixed them up in wild ways. The most successful dance of all was when he called out all the moony young boys and girls who were going steady, and when they were all dutifully arranged on the floor he made them all change partners. The delighted uproar from the town at the long sad faces of the steadies being deprived of their true loves, broke down any lingering resistance. There was no longer any need of the impostor. The only remaining worry was that the stomping and the booming on the floorboards was going to cause the rickety restaurant to start working its way off the supports and slide down into the bayou.

"Oh, you big fat preacher," a woman called as she swirled and sashayed by us with explosive force, "you can get a body goin'."

"Almost as good as religion, isn't it?" Demara said.

"It's a hell of a lot better," her husband shouted back.

Demara stepped down from the little bandstand. "I think we had better get moving." He nodded to the young leader who was now in complete command, calling out orders and maneuvering the whirling, flying couples as if he were counting change in the palm of his hand. Demara winked at him. "Learn something?" he asked.

"Never forget it," the boy said, and fixed the impostor with a shy smile.

Outside it was cool and refreshing after the sweaty rush of humanity in the wooden hall. We went down onto a gravel walk that led to the edge of the bayou, and even despite the thumping of the bass, the twang of a country guitar thrumming and an occasional scream like the Yanks must have heard at Shiloh, we could hear the soft gentle sound of the wind shifting through the moss-draped cypress and oak in the swamp.

"Now that was nice of you," I finally said.

"That wasn't nice. Don't you go and get soft on me. I was just keeping the old hand in." We went back down to the Death Wagon. When we didn't need it to, it started up at once.

"No. I've thought about it. That was a good thing," I said.

"I won't say it was good, that's something else," he finally said, and then I saw him smile. "But I had it, didn't I?"

"You really had it," I agreed.

"You know something? It feels good to have it. I can't deny that. I really had them stompin' and roarin' and shoutin', didn't I?"

"You *really* had them."

"Anyway, they had fun," he apologized. "You know how I know when I have it?" I asked how.

"They always begin to think of me as a preacher." I let out a laugh of recognition because it was so true about him. "And you know what's even funnier? When I see myself in a mirror I'm surprised to find I don't have a turned collar on."

The plan was to enter Texas by the most implausible route possible so that our chances of meeting a Texas Ranger or state trooper were more than slim. From the southern rice country I turned the car west and a little north for Texas.

"No, that *was* a good thing," I said once more. "Even if you were just keeping your hand in or practicing your technique, the end result was good."

"Gave you a peek at the other Demara, didn't I. You should have seen him sometimes," he said.

"I can imagine. Well, I'm glad we stayed."

"Glad, hell. I wouldn't have missed it." He laughed with enormous relish. "I always did want to go to a square dance. That was my first, you know."

That was the impostor in full form. I felt much better about the future. Texas seemed to lose much of its terrors. We were not much more than one hundred miles away and the flag of his spirit was unfurled and waving on high.

12.

I had given my word that I would call Judy at exactly eleven o'clock, New York time, that night. I had failed her several times on these calls, which she termed "tragically urgent." Since she had finally been good enough to arrange for my clothes to catch up with me in care of General Delivery, Chicago, I had vowed I wouldn't fail on my call this time. I placed the call from Hope, Arkansas.

"Oh, thank God, Bob," Judy said. Before I had a chance to ask how she was and how the children were, I was greeted by a male voice on the other end of the phone.

"Crichton?"

"Yes, sir," I said.

"Webster, here. Dr. Webster. Your wife has told you all about me."

She hadn't, in fact, ever mentioned his name.

"Oh, yes, of course," I said. "Don't tell me. It's going to be twins. Or is it a Caesarean section?"

"I am Webster. Dr. Webster."

"Oh," I lied again. "I'm not hearing you well."

"I-am-the-psychoanalyst," Dr. Webster said. "I am not worried about your wife." He paused. "I am not worried about your children." He paused. "I am worried about *you*."

I mumbled something about being gratified and he added:

"My colleagues are worried about you!"

The picture of a roomful of analysts discussing one's soul is flattering.

"Is it safe for you to talk?" Dr. Webster asked. I told him I didn't know what he meant.

"The psychotic with you," he said impatiently. "Is he out of the way? Is he under control?"

I could see Fred from the phone booth, having a chocolate soda, regaling the young man behind the counter with some tale. I assured the doctor that Demara seemed under control.

"Now pay attention to me. This man . . . this impostor you are traveling with . . . this is a dangerous man. He is not what he seems to be."

It caused me to snort, just once.

"Pay attention," Webster said.

"Yes, pay attention, Bob, for God's sake," Judy said on the extension.

Doctor Webster began to outline the nature of the compulsive, addicted impostor. The sum of his argument, at least as it pertained to me and my future safety, was that the impostor desperately despised what he felt to be his real self. One might go so far, at least Dr. Webster went so far, as saying that the act of exchanging one's identity was the ritualistic equivalent of self-murder. As a new person, under a new identity, the impostor was capable of momentarily deluding himself and acting with the confidence and self-assurance and ability his own identity denied him. It was highly dangerous, however, the doctor was telling me, to probe into the first, real identity. It was quite feasible that as the prober—me—learned more and more of the real person, just to that degree did I become identified with the real person. Finally, when the impostor's compulsion to destroy his real image became strong enough, it just might be necessary for the impostor to destroy me, either figuratively or for real.

I gasped slightly, and I could hear Judy. She was very upset.

"Now I mean this quite seriously. The more you learn about this subject, the more you are placing your life in jeopardy," Webster went on. "And the more he *knows* you know about him, just that much more will he sooner or later feel he must do something—ah, permanent about you."

"Like kill me."

"In non-technical terms, yes," Dr. Webster said.

I knew then more clearly than ever before that, whether Webster were exaggerating or not, that my orange notebook must stay hidden from Demara's eyes at any cost.

But it all seemed so unreal then. There he was, his hands shaping out some part of his story, a smile creasing his large face, and the clerk doubled over with laughter.

"Has he so far gone through a very moody phase?" I was asked. I admitted that indeed he had.

"What about drinking?" I told him heavy. I wondered if he'd read my letters home.

"Has he ever gone through long periods where he feels he isn't really worthy?" Who hasn't, I thought, but admitted that the "subject" did this, too.

The doctor wanted to know if, and how, Demara might suffer from feelings of insecurity, exhibiting them through deep feelings of anxiety and exaggerated expectations.

I thought about Texas. Only that morning Demara had warned me that if the Rangers or the troopers roughed us up that I must handle myself like a man and earn their respect because if I broke, they would be merciless.

Were those fears exaggerated or not? I knew this much; Demara had seen some hard, tough, wicked doings in Texas jails. If one felt this was to be one's fate, could a psychiatrist say a fear of it was exaggerated?

"So you will agree that our appraisal of the subject would seem to meet with reality?"

I had to agree that it did. The counterman had gone away to handle another customer and I saw Demara's smiling face collapse into a moody frown.

We talked about my duty to leave the "subject" when and if I sensed he was nearing a breaking point. I tried to explain that a good deal of Demara's unrest stemmed from a fear of going to Texas.

"But why must he *go* to Texas?" the doctor asked. It

was one of those questions that can only be called "a good question."

"Part of his self-destructive syndrome," I said. What else could I say.

"Why, of course," Dr. Webster said.

I could see Demara waving at me frantically now, and the sight of it saddened me. He *was* nearing the breaking point.

"I'll take care," I promised, and hung up. When I came out of the booth he grabbed my arm and powered me to the door. His powerful grip intimated to me a latent hostility which could only be interpreted as wishing that I were dead.

"What the hell were you doing there?" he said. I said something rather pointless.

"What do you think I was waving about, for God's sake? I made them keep the store open an extra ten minutes just so you could blab about nothing on the phone."

13.

I couldn't wake him. For the first time since we had gone on the road, I was up before the impostor. I nudged him but got no response and I had to watch the mound of blankets a long time before being satisfied that what lay beneath them was alive. When I came back from breakfast he still had not moved and it wasn't until the motel keeper warned me that another day's rent would be due if we weren't gone within the hour that I was able to rouse him.

He said nothing to me. I don't think he was capable of speech then. The flag of his spirit that had been flying so high the day before was now faintly fluttering, unfurled at half mast. When the Death Wagon failed to start and I had to ask him to push the car to an incline, a thing that often before had ruined an entire day, he made no protest but did as he was asked. I was stunned by the change in the man beside me. He seemed altogether immobilized. I knew he was conscious of me watching him but I could not control myself. On the day that I had kidnapped him he had acted this way but I was never sure that that hadn't been an elaborate joke. I was a little horrified when he began to mumble something and, finally, speak up quite loudly. I recognized it as a quote but I didn't know from what.

"'Play the man, Master Ridley,'" Demara said. "'we shall this day light such a candle, by God's grace, in England, as I trust shall never be out.'"

The voice had been loud and even alive, but about the rest of him was a quality of death.

"Hugh Latimer said that to the boy, Ridley, when they were about to be burned at the stake for heresy."

It was increasingly clear that we were approaching Texas by the growing number of road signs. The low, flat land began to blossom with ads for CRISPER'S Hot Shot Nerve Tonic and GROVE'S CHILL TONIC. There were old weathered signs for 666, good for the swamp chills and ague, and Dr. Pepper, to be drunk at 10, 2 and 4.

"That's the way I want to go—like Latimer, proud and sudden," Demara said, and smacked his fist into his hand, the first evidence of life I had seen. "After all, what can they do to you? A few minutes' pain, and immortality. But don't think it won't hurt," he warned me. "These people are *mean*."

We were back in cotton country. The day was cold and wet and smoke wound up from little wooden, sway-roofed shacks that looked as if no one had lived in them for twenty years. We never once saw a human being. When I looked back at Demara he had slumped once again into this strange, catatonic condition. People suffering attacks of dementia praecox generally act this way. What the outcome of it might be I didn't know but it worried me. I wished that I could call Dr. Webster.

"Don't you worry about me," Demara suddenly said,

in a deep, rumbly voice, expending as little energy as possible. It made me blush. Was I that transparent? "This is nature's way of protecting me," he explained. "She's conserving my resources for the ordeal ahead."

I realized then that my worries about Demara, at least then, were exaggerated. He has some very reassuring thoughts about the order of things. He sees Fate and Mother Nature as personal deities who can be on his side or be against him in a very intimate way. When he feels they are getting in back of him, he has a powerful asset going for him. He would have made a grand Greek!

He shivered and breathed deeply, trying to throw off the catatonic coils that bound him.

"The ice of Texas is upon me," he said, apologetically, and he seemed much better.

"Look, I want to repeat this now. If they try and do anything to you, don't give them an inch. They'll respect you then and take it easy. But if you howl or crawl, they'll pistol-whip you good. So that'll be our own code. 'Play the man, Master Ridley.' That'll buck us both up."

I continued to resent being made a part of the whole action, but I told Demara that I honestly didn't feel that I could endure a pistol whipping without crying out.

"You'll learn," he assured me. "Or you better learn. I'm going to explain it to you for the last time; these people are *mean*."

For the first time on the trip I began to feel myself as part of the operation. No longer did I have that old vantage point of being a part of things but always nicely divorced from them; in for all the fun, free from all the pain. If these people were as mean as Demara insisted they were, there was no real reason they wouldn't work me over, along with my buddy, and listen to complaints later. I began to get increasingly nervous and tense myself, although, as Fred tried to explain why the people would be mean, I began learning a good deal about Demara when he was Ben Jones, assistant prison warden.

The Texas prison system, run by Mr. O. B. Ellis, an import from Tennessee, is one of the best-run prison systems in the nation. It also, however, is severely hamstrung by one of the most reactionary, antiquated and anachronistic governing bodies left this side of ancient feudal conclaves. The Texas legislature sees a prison system as a place of punishment for crimes committed, not as a place to rehabilitate broken lives. You go there to hurt. One result of this policy is that Texas leads the nation in the rate of returnees. They go out hard and bitter and come back the same way, usually right away. Another result is that Texas is the only state whose prison population exceeds in growth her civilian population; and Texas is booming. One of the last serious efforts to rewrite the basic penal philosophy was voted down when it was asserted that the next thing the reformers would want to do is to re-write the holy Bible. That ended that debate. Another result is that Texas, saddled with a professional, hard-core, hard-case, hard-ass, as they say, prison population is forced to hire some of the hardest-eyed, coldest-souled citizens in the state to be their prison guards. These shotgun toting people have become identified in Demara's mind with what he means when he says Texans. There is no doubt that some of these men are, indeed, *mean.*

"And I mean *mean,*" Demara often says.

The fact that Demara, as Jones, not only survived but prospered in the prison system is an impressive commentary on him as either man.

"The only worry now is whether they'll take us as we go across the border or play cat and mouse with us."

"Oh, come on," I said. "You can't honestly believe they've got every road in East Texas covered just for little old you and me?"

This stung him.

"If you're implying that I'm acting like an overly apprehensive child, don't bother. Who the hell were you talking to last night?" he asked me. For the second time that morning I blushed. He fortunately let it drop.

"You told O. B. Ellis we'd be arriving at just about this time. Correct?" I nodded that that was so.

"Then he knows where we are right now, and if he doesn't he will after we've been in Texas two hours."

We passed out of the stretch of cotton country back into some swamp lands. Along the border they become known as baygalls, special Texas-type swamps loaded with bay trees and clumped up with inkberry bushes, and the signs, which Demara hadn't noticed before, began again.

"I could use some of that Hot Shot Nerve Tonic," I said.

"I could use that Grove's Chill Tonic." He pointed out a large, greenish sign. "That's the one we're really going to be needing soon," he said ominously. It read:

SLAUGHTERINE—FOR PAIN

Although he carried himself as a man with a rendezvous

with destiny, and seemingly had abandoned himself to his fate, somewhere the instinct for survival still goaded him. At his command we left the main road heading toward Texarkana and took a side road south.

"There's an old back country road that goes across the border just north of the Sulphur River. There won't be anyone there." The road we were on was barely passable. Although hard-topped it was so coated with mud from farm vehicles coming in from the mud-deep side roads that at times one couldn't tell it was paved. We wound through the baygalls, over little wooden bridges where men were fishing for bass, past stretches of cotton fields that soon would be worked, until I was completely confused. It occurred to me that for all of the impostor's romantic illusions of his destiny, he must have done, as always, some deep, thorough and imaginative advance work on how to hold that destiny off. Where he had done it I had no idea but no one could have charted a route through those dismals without having recourse to some elaborate charts. I wondered what Webster would make of this.

"Enjoy it!" Demara warned me. "It won't be long now."

The whole thing kept reminding me of a gospel song I had heard a few days before along the road in Arkansas: "Be Happy With What You Got Today" (Because Hell Ain't But a Mile and a Quarter Away).

"*There she lies!*" Demara suddenly shouted out. "It's her!" And he went into a complete coma. Up ahead along the road, perhaps a quarter of a mile away, I could see a state highway sign. I felt my stomach suddenly give away beneath me, like it always had before a football game

when the coach would break the death-like silence of the
locker room by looking at his watch and saying "All
right, boys. This is the big one. Let's go." Only there was no
coach to lean on or to troop behind. The man with me had
submerged himself behind some incredibly effective psychological shield.

The impostor was catatonic.

Near the border was a sprawling field filled with the
brown stalks of last year's cotton. One patch of the field
had not been harvested and wet but white globs of cotton still clung to dead bolls. I asked Demara's permission
to stop and look at the cotton and when he gave no sign
that he heard me I pulled the car over to the side of the
road and went down into the field. I could understand why
no one had been out plowing although by northern
standards the season was ripe for the blade. The field was
steeped in mud, a thick, reddish, glue-like gumbo that had
the textual feeling of wet concrete. At every step it tried
to tear my shoes off.

"Sap!" Demara called out the window of the car. I had
not been sure he was alive.

The cotton fascinated me and I was astonished at how
much raw cotton a single plant held. In spite of the mud
I pulled up several more plants to take home for the children, and, in that deep, I went down the line and pulled
up a number more for them to take to school and show
their classmates.

"Stupid!"

I stumbled and clawed my way back up onto the road.
A few days before a deep swamp logger had voluntarily
ripped open the trunk of the car with a crow bar and

logging chain so that the trunk, after being jammed shut for years, now was wide open, flying open and shut with every jounce. I put the cotton plants in the trunk and got back into the car.

"Fool!" Demara said. "That mud will never come off your shoes for the rest of their days."

I don't know why I felt he didn't know what he was talking about. I chose to forget the months he had spent as a prison captain, running strings of prisoners out into cotton fields and pea patches like this, "ridin' shotgun" over them.

"Those shoes will have to be washed with a brush right now or they will be ruined," he said, and his eyes closed and he became once more the immobile, inscrutable, comatose Buddha. "It won't be long now," he mumbled. I began whistling *Hell Ain't But a Mile and a Quarter*.

When we drove across the Texas border a few minutes later he didn't notice it. A small sign announced that we were now in that contentious land. Texas looked as cordial and lonely as Arkansas had been and I was feeling vastly relieved when my heart thudded hollowly in my chest and I felt myself tighten. As we came around a bend, up ahead at an old weighing station that must have been used to spot-check truck weight loads, was a Texas state trooper car. I had a first wild impulse to stop and get it over with.

"Here we are. Do with us as you will, sir."

The impostor came bolt awake. I knew he would.

"Oh, God," he said.

As we reached the car I slowed to a decent speed and as I passed the car I nodded politely to the trooper. He noticed our out-of-state plate and said "Welcome to Texas."

"The hypocritical bastard," Demara said.

I tried to get a look at the state trooper through the rear view mirror but the view was blocked by the trunk door which kept bobbing up and down.

"So, it's going to be a game of cat and mouse," Demara said. "So they're going to play it that way. All right," he said, "if they want to play, we'll play with them. These people can be mean, and so can we," he assured me. The passive-resistance Buddha had rejoined the fight and it made me feel better. There was the light of life in his eyes and he was animated again.

"There's a road up ahead of here that turns off to the right, heading north. We're going to take that road. Step on it," he ordered.

Since I couldn't see the police behind me I was chary about speeding up but I pressed a little harder on the accelerator and was pleased the way the old car still responded.

"We're in Texas, all right," Demara said, pointing out the window. "Look. Chinaberry trees."

I kept my eyes fixed firmly on the road. Since the speedometer was broken I had no idea of our speed but I judged it now at possibly seventy miles an hour.

"I think this is the wrong thing to be doing," I said.

"Pour it on," Demara said. "Oh, we're going to give these mean bastards a run for it," he said, chuckling.

And that was when we heard the siren.

It was a long, screaming whine that came like a needle into the heart of my ear. For a moment I alternated between panicking altogether and doing nothing. As a result, I froze.

"Do something," Demara shouted at me. I couldn't. "Slow down," he cried.

The Death Wagon ran along, out of my command.

"I mean it," Demara shouted again. "Pull over before he shoots."

I felt his foot cross my mud-coated foot and mash down on the brake pedal. It was enough to start the car slowing and I was finally able to get enough grasp of myself to begin guiding it over to the side of the road. The trooper was alongside me by now.

"*Get over there!*" he commanded. I wanted to say Yes, sir. Nothing came.

"He will, he will," Demara was saying.

He let up the pressure on my foot.

"God Almighty," he breathed. "He might have shot. I told you they were mean."

The state trooper had pulled far ahead of us on the road and even as I was still steering in to park behind him he was clambering out of the car.

I wanted only one thing then. That was to think of the code, that heroic saying that would give me courage in the time of crisis. It eluded me and I looked to Demara. He was gone again, locked away within himself, drawing on his own resources for the ultimate struggle that lay ahead.

"Play what?" I asked him.

The trooper was crossing the concrete, coming for the car, taking long, purposeful strides.

"Play what? Play the what?" I demanded. "What was the thing you told me to say?" I pulled on Demara but he was unmovable.

I watched the pistol wash back and forth with each long stride. He was a tall man. He looked mean. He looked as if he were heading for the showdown gunfight at the OK Corral.

All I could think of was "You may fire when ready, Gridley," and that wasn't right.

The trooper stopped perhaps a dozen feet from the old car and stared at it. He studied it from every angle and then shook his head.

"Lord help us," Demara whispered. "This is it."

I could no longer see the trooper clearly because of the salt from the sweat which was coursing down my brow and into my eyes.

"I wouldn't have believed it could go that fast," the trooper said. He was talking about the Death Wagon. Neither of us said anything.

"You were hitting close to seventy-five in this old can," he remarked. It suddenly came to me; the code words, and I said them aloud.

"Play the man, Master Ridley," I said.

"What's that?" the trooper said.

"Shut up," Demara hissed at me.

The Texan's narrowed, hard, pale-blue eyes studied us.

"You boys *knowed* you was being bad," he said, quietly.

"Yes, sir," I said.

"No, sir," Demara said.

"You boys *knowed* you was breaking the law," he said, almost sweetly.

"He's waiting to pounce," Demara whispered.

"My speedometer was broken, officer—" I began.

"It's a mighty serious charge," he began.

"Oh, I know that," I said.

"Will you shut your mouth?" Demara said.

"And the fine is $1000 and six months in jail or both," the trooper said. Demara was getting out of the car.

"Look, officer, let's end this little charade. If you have your warrant, present it. Otherwise, go get one."

"I don't need a warrant," he said. "You got the evidence stickin' out all over you."

"All right, spare the cracks," Demara said. I noticed, however, that he tried to pull himself together. "Yes, my name is Ferdinand W. Demara. But what's the charge?"

"I don't care who you are," the trooper said. "The charge is transportin' Arkansas cotton across the state border of Texas."

He skipped around to the back of the car where the trunk was almost filled with the brownish green stalks and leaves of Arkansas cotton plants. He came back and waggled the foliage in our faces.

"You going to try and deny the evidence?" he said. For a long moment we boggled at each other and then began grinning.

"Now you can play the man, Master Ridley," Demara said. When I saw the trooper poking through the cotton plants I was forced to begin laughing in earnest.

"Nothing to laugh at," the trooper said. His steel-like grip was around my arm and it calmed me fast. "This Arkansas cotton, it's sick. It's diseased. Isn't clean and sturdy like our Texas crop." He held the plants away from him as if they were catching and the plague was upon them.

"If I thought you people were Southerners and knew what you was doing, I'd drag you in."

We were free, and I felt a refreshing feeling of escaping something dreadful when I heard Demara.

"I *am* a Southerner," he said, in a miserable accent. "My name is Ben W. Jones, I'm a Texan and you want to know my trouble?"

The ice-blue eyes drilled into us.

"My trouble is I'm ashamed of it."

"Get this man out of here," the trooper said, a strong hint of color rising up behind the leathery complexion. "You get him movin'."

I prodded the impostor to his side of the car and pushed him into the front seat. The car didn't start and I had to ask the trooper for a push. He didn't seem to mind since he was very pleased with his detective work.

"I knew you boys was up to *something* bad. And it is," he said, piling the cotton in the back of his car, "a mighty serious thang."

When he had left us to take the diseased plants back to Arkansas I turned on Demara in a rage but he refused to get embroiled with me.

"That's the first gun, the Fort Sumter you might say," he said. "They're going to get us but the least we can do is go down fighting." I tried to argue with him to no avail at all that the trooper hadn't the least idea who we were. I felt he had been uncommonly courteous.

"The Great Harassment has begun," he insisted. "I did think that last one was pretty good. 'My trouble is, I'm from Texas and I'm ashamed of it.' Did you study the look on his face?"

The brush with the law had seemed to calm him. Now that in his mind the first blood had been shed, as so often happens in war or athletics, the rest was a little easier than the ungodly chore of waiting for the unknown.

"Oh, don't think that O. B. Ellis won't be chuckling about this little fiasco tonight. I just hope he gets that crack, too."

We turned up the road leading north, doubled back on another spur heading west, and dipped south again, always heading south and west towards Huntsville.

We had already seen a classic American example of name corruption along the road. Out in the sandy, pine-studded hills we passed a number of mailboxes bearing the name of Brooktrout. As we neared the towns the name became Booktrout and Bucktroud and, in the towns, several times we saw the name Buchtraudt. Names, as they must, interest the impostor. But then somewhere along the road, in a little thorp outside of Nacogdoches, we came upon the name of Muckleroy.

Muckleroy! It is a name that Dickens would have taken to his heart. It is a good American name; it has the genuine American *smack* to it. One especially intrigued him. This was H. Muckleroy.

"I like to think it's Hosmer. Hosmer Muckleroy. Actually Fanshaw would be better. Or Henry. Henry Wadsworth Muckleroy."

He tried to put combinations together while we drove. "H.H.H," he mused. When we passed a man out on the highway getting his mail from a rural mailbox Demara ordered me to stop the car. "I've *got* to find out what that H stands for."

"You mean that H. Muckleroy on the sign back in town?" the man asked. He scratched his head and through squinted eyes stared way across the flat, rolling country.

"Oh, yes," he said. "Yes, indeed, you must mean ol' Huck. Yes, indeed, you mean Huck Muckleroy."

Demara began to chortle with uncontainable glee.

"Oh, it's great. It's marvelous." The man appeared to be bewildered and even hurt.

"Well, it's not his *real* name," the man said apologetically.

"Ah, an impostor," Demara said.

"It's just short for Huckleberry, you know," the man said.

Huckleberry Muckleroy!

It has since become our rallying cry. Gone is Master Ridley. When things look very down and very dark the mere mention of Huckleberry Muckleroy is enough to put everything in balance again.

It has, also, become the ultimate acid test for Demara as impostor. Some day he has sworn he is going to dare it. Already, I know, he has started work on it. He has collected a few of Mr. Muckleroy's credentials. He will consider it the star in his constellation of characters the day he gets the brass and mastery to pass himself off to the world as Huckleberry Muckleroy. If he can get away with that, he will have entered the ranks of the immortals.

The original plan had been to drive into Huntsville, if we weren't stopped before then, and stay in a small motel near the outskirts of the town. As we drove down out of the Big Thicket, a wild, swampy, sandy wilderness stretch that few men have ever mastered, into Huntsville, darkness had fallen. The lights hovered over the walls of the prison but Demara would not allow me to even slow down.

"You've got to keep going, keep going, keep going," he said. He held himself still, as if were he even to move a muscle something would break, and we drove straight through the town. It looked very much like a clean, small, Midwestern college town. We stayed instead in Conroe, a rough, rural and ready oil and lumber town mainly famous for its suburb, the infamous hamlet of Cut 'n' Shoot, Texas. The name speaks for itself.

When we arrived a peculiar bit of business was being unfolded. In the state legislature the day before one of the local legislators had introduced a bill which would outlaw all naturopaths. Naturopaths are a Texas specialty, semi-legitimate herb and nature healers who dabble in everything from organic soils to religio-mysticism to effect cures. On the very next day, however, the same legislator had introduced a bill recommending that all naturopaths not only not be outlawed but that they be formally endorsed and fully licensed to practice by Texas. At the time we entered a local restaurant, just across the street from the Crighton Theatre (another outlandish corruption of a name), the battle was raging as to just how big a bundle of greenbacks the very popular legislator must have gotten in order to make such a switch. One local naturopath was telling one and all that it had cost them plenty to "convert" the man.

That night was an uncomfortable one. Since O. B. Ellis

had treated Demara like a father would treat a son, the impostor has an unusually sharp feeling of guilt about the Texas masquerade.

"How he must hate me," Demara insisted. "How the very thought of me must make him sick."

I had talked to Mr. Ellis on the phone and hadn't felt this reaction, but Demara would not believe me. He began to drink again.

All of that night we sat in a little motel room, the rain pouring down outside and the rum running steadily inside, and Demara insisted on cataloging all the unworthy things he had ever done. He exaggerates the unworthiness of what he has done because he doubts his own motivation. If he wants to do it, then it must be bad. When I later checked some of these incidents with the people they happened to they had no memory of them or didn't feel they had been wronged at all. I wondered if he was really beginning to crack apart. I fell asleep while he talked and I don't know how long he might have continued, but in the morning he was no better.

I had arranged to drive to Huntsville and meet with Mr. O. B. Ellis that morning and as I headed for the door, trying to leave as quietly as possible, he suddenly blocked my way.

"Don't go. Please. I ask this respect of you," he said. I knew it was mandatory that I go, and when he continued to block the door I simply went back into the back bedroom, opened the screen and climbed out. I felt he would be enraged at my trick but he didn't seem to notice it.

"He'll only give you a distorted idea of me. He *has* to lie to cover himself."

I told him that I was an experienced reporter who had some training at being able to tell which version of a story seemed most correct. That seemed to calm him, but then he suddenly leaped in front of the car.

"You'll have to run me down," he shouted at me. He stood with his arms outstretched, his bottle of rum held out like the torch on the Statue of Liberty. It was very bold and effective except that he probably knew as well as I that the Death Wagon wouldn't start without a push.

He sat in front of the car for a while, drinking, and all at once surrendered.

"Don't you have a better suit than that?" My suit was dreadfully spotted. "I can't have Ellis think my biographer is a bum." I told him it was the best I had and then he asked me to make one supreme gesture for him. He wanted me to rent a brand new, spanking fresh car just for the day.

Money was by now becoming a pressing thing which I as yet hadn't the nerve to discuss with him. The rental would hurt, and then I thought of an out. If Mr. Ellis' spy system was so effective, then he would already know about the old car and see through the feeble effort to gain respectability.

"Would you want O. B. Ellis to think that you were a common, bourgeois, middle-class fraud who trys to buy status by a car?" I said. He denied it vigorously.

"Although it is the truth," he added.

We made a splendid compromise finally. I wasn't to wear my suit but was to get decked out in my sports coat with the elbow patches and the baggy flannels and play the Greenwich Village artist.

"That way they'll have no standard for you," Demara said. "They'll even be afraid of you."

Although Texans claim to revel in characters, it is Demara's contention that nothing scares a Texan like a true character.

"If they can't type you, they're terrified."

When I came out from changing my clothes, the new role pleased him.

"My, you look dreadful," he said, admiringly. "Come on, I'll even give you a push. Oh," he added, "be sure to put on that English accent you use. It gives them an inferiority complex."

The interview with Mr. Ellis was a success. Far from what Demara felt, the people at the prison were generous about him. Demara, to them, was the impostor, and only Ben W. Jones was real in their minds. I was taken on a tour of the prison. Although it is very clearly run as a model prison the sight of seeing so many thousands of young, often intelligent, energetic lives locked away is always such a shock that I'm not much good at appraising what I see in a prison. If this is the best solution we can manage, then somewhere we must be failing. The maximum security section, the section of the prison where Demara worked, is even more depressing because this is the place where they keep the men who, for the most part, have almost completely lost the ability to make any kind of compromise with any form of life. Many of them learned this in jail, some because they were mad. It was here, however, that Demara had excelled.

When I started back to Conroe I was happy. Whatever doubts I had secretly had about Demara as the *great* impostor for the most part vanished. Here, in admittedly one of the toughest, most difficult cell blocks in the United States, Demara had performed with distinction. No longer was there any hint of romanticizing. I had talked with hardened guards and nonromantic prisoners. All had agreed that Demara, as Jones, had made real accomplishments and had proved himself as a man of parts in a place where men are watched closely and judged harshly. One of his weapons was intelligence; another was a certain instinctive understanding of the convict as outcast and misfit; and another technique, one inaccessible to cowards, was gentleness. One prison official had said to me:

"Why, you know how I used to think of Jones? I used to see him as a great big ol' Teddy bear."

I thought that would amuse him.

When I got back to Conroe I parked the car on a hill a few hundred feet from the motel and ran all the way to the cabin. The door was locked. I went around to the windows, and, although it was a steaming hot day, the windows were locked and the blinds drawn. I was worried.

"Fred," I called. "It's me. Crichton."

"Who's with you?" he called back.

"No one," I answered, but he made me stand out in the middle of the parking area while he peeked through the blinds and checked all around the cabin. When he was satisfied that I was alone I could hear the grating sound of furniture being moved, and then the door swung quickly open.

"Hurry," he cried. "Inside."

It was oppressive and steaming in the cabin, but he shut the door and closed the blinds. Was this the phase that Doctor Webster had warned about? He seemed in an extremely agitated state. He slapped a copy of the local paper into my hands.

"My God, read it!" he ordered.

The story was one that one might expect would emanate from the country of Cut 'n' Shoot.

Sometime that morning, at about six o'clock, just as the mist was rising from lawns and the sun was coming out, a resident of the area had responded to a knock on his door. When he opened it, he had been bathed by a bucket of acid.

"A *bucket,* for God's sake. Did you read it? A *bucket.* Oh, I told you, I told you," he said, slumping back down into his chair and pulling at the rum bottle by his side. "These people are so *mean.*"

He stared rather helplessly and dramatically into a little electric fan he had found.

"Right down the road from here." He shook his head again and again. "In New York they use a *vial.* All they need to blind a man there is a *vial.* Down here they have to use a *bucket.* That's the way they are. It won't do to blind me, they have to disintegrate me. Because that was meant for me."

I didn't answer that. I felt he was suffering a mild case of self-pity mixed with rum, a certain anxiety, fear of what Ellis might have told me, and normal hallucinations occasioned by Texas.

"That acid was meant for me. Don't try and tell me otherwise. I know what you're thinking."

I was thinking that if he only slowed down on the rum somewhat things might arrange themselves in better focus.

"The paper admits there was no motive. They are so goddamned *right* there's no motive. Because I—Ben W. Jones or Demara, whichever one it is they think they're destroying—am the motive. They had the right idea, just the wrong door."

"I don't say it was Ellis. God, no," he said shortly after this. "But I do say it was some psychopathic assistant of Ellis who wants to show the chief what a sterling man of action he is." I couldn't discuss this madness with him.

"Why? I'll tell you why. It all goes back to the bucket. Why a *bucket,* in the name of God? Once you see me as the motive though, it's all so clear. Obliterate my face. Burn off my fingerprints. Rot the flesh from over my bones, and they can say I never existed. Simple, isn't it? No Demara, no disgrace."

I had a second appointment with Mr. Ellis and the people at the prison. I hated to leave him that way, cowering in the cabin, drinking deep of the flaming rum, convinced that hired killers armed with buckets of acid were seeking his flesh, but I had to get out.

As I started for the car I turned back when I heard his voice.

"A word of warning," he said.

I couldn't see him. The voice was clear but far-away sounding and hollow.

"Answer no knocks on no doors!"

The last sound I heard was that of furniture being moved back into position.

When I came back from the prison, the motel lay sleeping in darkness. There was a wind that shifted and hushed through the loblolly pines outside our cabin. We had neglected to make any advance signal for recognition and I was afraid to knock for fear that Demara, if his persecution reactions were as keen as they seemed to be getting, might have his own welcome for those who knocked. I had read about a detective who had been shot coming to give aid to a person who was convinced the Mafia were after him. At the first knock, the man fired, killing his rescuer. I suspicioned that Demara was packing a gun, but I had never seen it. I didn't want to test the point.

I tried to think of some tune I could whistle that would identify me. I tried "With Crimson In Triumph Flashing" and "Fair Harvard" to no avail, and finally I just scratched on the screen of a window.

"Who is it?" he said in a hoarse whisper.

"It's me," I said. "Huckleberry Muckleroy."

Despite the tenseness there was a roar of laughter, and then I heard piece after piece of furniture being dragged back from the door before it opened.

"Come in, Huck," he said. "I thought you were never going to come. It's been terrible."

We looked around at the disorder in the room.

"I had a feeling it was going to come by fire," he finally said. "By the time I could have moved this furniture away I would have been reduced to char."

His ability to romanticize himself in even a trying time suddenly struck me as ludicrous.

"Anyone else would be reduced to an ash. You have to be reduced to a char."

"I don't like to think of myself as an ash. Nobody does," he said.

By the telltale mound of cigarette butts stacked in a sea shell by his side, I could gather that he had spent the entire time sitting in his chair, drinking his Demarara rum, waiting, like the Swede in Hemingway's *The Killers,* for his bath of acid.

I went around the room turning on lights while he protested and opening blinds and even leaving the front door wide open to get rid of the odor of rum and the feeling of fear and heat.

Char, indeed, I thought. With all that 150-proof rum in him, if there had been a flame, there would have been an explosion. Flame would have flashed out of every orifice in his body. He would have been propelled. A human rocket trying to stagger into orbit, ricocheting around the room like a runaway Roman candle ball, going phffft, phffft, phffft every time he breathed, thundering into a new direction the way a balloon does when the air is released. Even now, I felt, there was a real danger that if Demara burped while lighting a cigarette, he might be consumed by a fireball.

The scream, one of the most chilling that I have ever heard, came from the bathroom. I managed to get by or jump over the things in the room and when I got to Demara he was both calling me for help and holding his assailant with a grip made strong by fear and anger and rum. I turned on the light and a moment later he shamefacedly slid his arms from around the thing. It wasn't actually as absurd as it might seem.

That morning I had hung up my suit in the bathroom to steam out the wrinkles. I had wrapped it in a full-length plastic cover. When Demara stumbled into the

bathroom, his arms reaching ahead of him, he unfortunately embraced the plastic bag. He at once realized
that he had either grabbed a hanging man or a naked
assassin. In either case he let out one of the most unearthly
screams.

"My God, I thought someone had committed suicide
in my bathroom."

Actually, the incident served to relieve the tension.
Gradually I began to feel that Demara's biggest fear was
not acid but the tongue of O. B. Ellis. He was afraid to
ask outright but little by little he began to probe me about
what his old colleagues had said about him.

"You didn't happen to meet a man named Clark by any
chance?" I let him know that I had.

"Nervous sort, did you notice? Of course, that's because
he's a pathological liar. Can't believe a word he says. I
guess you noticed that? Well, what did *he* have to say?"

When I told him Clark had nothing but complimentary
things to say about him, he seemed vastly relieved. Man
by man he edged up the ladder toward Mr. Ellis. As he
passed each rung, Demara seemed to expand and become
his old self and even grow cocky. It was late when we
finally got around to Ellis.

I told Demara how Mr. Ellis had agreed that Demara
had done some fine work, that there had been a real future
for him in the prison system and that, if only Demara
could come along in some complete new guise, that he
would be glad to have him back in the prison system.

"In fact," I said, "he said he always thought of you as
just a great, big, ol' Teddy bear."

"He said that," Demara said, quietly.

"That's right. That you reminded him of a big, charming roly-poly bear who wouldn't hurt a fly," I added, cheerily.

"A Teddy bear," Demara mumbled. *"He* said *I* was a Teddy bear?"* He was hurt, I could see that, and he was angry. His pride had taken a furious fall but I wasn't capable then of seeing just how far.

"A great big ol' Teddy bear," he shouted out loud. "Me. The man who went into the maximum security cells when no other man had ever done it before. He calls that a Teddy bear? Me, the man who could guarantee the prisoners could eat together. Why? Because I was the only one who could handle them, that's why."

He went over to the large, canvas bag he carried with him but rarely opened in my presence and slid something out of it.

"Get in the car," he shouted at me. "There's going to be some big trouble in Texas."

He kicked over a chair that was in his way and then angrily flung the bottle he was drinking out of across the room where it shattered with a crashing thump against a metal shower stall, spewing rum and glass around the room.

"I'll show those miserable bastards down there who's a Teddy bear. *Try and make me look ridiculous."*

His face was purple from rage and excitement and drinking, and I was worried he was going to suffer some kind of shock or stroke.

"If that was a gun I saw, I'm not going," I said. I was

truly afraid, but I was also conscious that this was the first time I had flatly disavowed Demara.

"We're going down there," he insisted, and he took my arm and began propelling me with enormous force toward the door. On the way out he kicked the top of my suitcase and kicked a hole right through it.

"Crummy leather," he had the gall to say.

"You might as well get your hands off me, Fred. You can't force me to drive you there. You know that."

He dropped my arm, and with a surprisingly agile leap he reached my suitcase, spilled the contents out onto the cluttered floor and with a shout of triumph held up the orange notebook. Then he took his weapon, a small-caliber pistol I didn't even want to look at, and flipped it across the room onto a bed.

"There," he said, washing his hands of the gun. "That satisfy you? Now," he said, holding up the book and beginning to flip through it, "If you want this back, throw me the keys to the car."

"I'll drive you down," I conceded. He threw the book to me and smiled triumphantly.

"We all have our Achilles heels, don't we?" he said.

I knew there was an extra bottle of rum stashed away in the glove compartment and I decided right then to risk it. If I opened it and encouraged him to keep drinking, I felt he stood a good chance of passing out. Despite the thrust from his rage, the general exhaustion of his body from the sleeplessness and the drinking of the previous days and nights was becoming apparent. He was staggering at times and I saw in his eyes the look of fatigue I had seen on the faces of infantrymen who were too long on the line.

"You'd better have some of this first," I said, and he smiled nicely.

"At last you're coming over to the right side."

He took a long, deep pull at the bottle. I did, too. It hit me like a little depth bomb going off somewhere down below. The explosion worked its way up from my stomach and spread out like a warm blast of air covering the upper part of my body. It was a dangerous game. Either the liquor would finally make him pass out or, if I miscalculated, cause him to go berserk.

I told him that the car would start but that we were almost out of gas and that I was going to get a five-gallon can. This was to give him more drinking time. He believed the story, and I was relieved to see him settle back in his seat and calm his rage with rum. I went up past the motel office and paid our bill, and then I scuttled down past the line of other dark cabins, came alongside our cabin and in full view of Demara, skittered into the cabin. Once inside I packed what I could as fast as possible. Occasionally I sneaked a look out the window at the impostor. He was drinking but staring far off, reaching, I hoped, a state of numbed euphoria. It occurred to me that if I were the acid bearer I could have washed him down to bones before he would have stirred. I took his gun and put it in my pocket.

"Gonna' see some justice done," he hollered out once.

I did my best to put the furniture back and to sweep up the broken rum bottle, and then I went back outside with his heavy bag and my broken-top suitcase and slid them in the trunk of the car. When I came around to the front of the car, he jumped.

"Don't sneak up on a man," he growled, but his eyes closed. I had a horrible urge to whisper something like bucket and Teddy bear in his ear, or acid, but I didn't dare.

Fortunately the Death Wagon started right up. Recently the gears had been sticking causing the car to lurch. It did as we started out of the motor court causing Demara, to my sadness, to wake but he only paused long enough to take another soul-filling swallow of rum. I settled down to drive as evenly and slowly and with as little motion as possible. Before we had gone a mile I heard his deep heavy raspy breathing. He sounded like a sawmill going into operation and later, when the breathing took on a more metallic note, like a section of a brass band warming up.

When we drove into Huntsville I was horrified by the bright, harsh glare of lights. The prison walls were flooded with light and it showered into the car almost as if it had weight. I was certain it would wake Demara. If he did make some kind of scene and we were stopped, I was the one most likely to go to jail. I had his gun and it felt enormous in my pocket. I could feel it burning there the way I had once felt a top burn which I stole from a five-and-ten-cent store. With my heart beating swiftly, I watched him for any sign that he was waking and it occurred to me with a shock that he looked like nothing more or less than a great big Teddy bear—fast asleep. There was no way I knew around the prison except to go right by it and as I slid along the walls, studying their bleak, doom-like length, I came within inches of running down an off-duty guard who shouted after me. Then as I tried to see him in the mirror, I came inches away from smashing into the trunk of a cruising patrol car. It was the driver of that car who informed me that my headlights were not on. At last we reached the end of the walls and finally the end of the flood-lit area and once more were back in blackness and out on the road to freedom.

For hour after hour I drove eastward while Demara slept away, and when we reached the Texas border I couldn't resist it. I began honking my horn in a jubilant manner and shouting "Good-by, Texas."

That roused the bear. He crawled up from his hibernation, growled several times and demanded to know what the hell happened to Huntsville. Somewhere, as I usually did, I had taken an incorrect turn. We were crossing the Red River into Little River County in Arkansas. That was the time for the gun. I opened my window and worked the weapon out of my pocket and let it fly into the dark waters of the Red River rushing below.

"What was that?" Demara asked.

"The end of an era," I said.

"Be sure to put *that* one in your notes," he said, and then asked me to drive slowly. I noticed with surprise that he was peering with intense concentration into the night. We passed through some ominous swamp country, into the back baygalls and bayous, and came out into cotton country again.

"Stop!" Demara commanded.

He got out of the car and disappeared in the blackness of the night. I could hear him snorting and chuffing down in the mud, and he sounded to me like a water buffalo. When he came back up onto the road his shoes were coated in mud, as mine still were. His arms were filled with uprooted cotton plants.

"I wouldn't be able to rest if I didn't do this. A man's got to be able to live with himself," he announced. "Back to Texas," he ordered.

We recrossed the Red River and drove on until Demara found what appeared to be a likely looking area. I parked the car so that the headlights shone out over a large Texas cotton field. I could see him out in it, moving among the stalks, shaking the cotton plants vigorously before strewing them all over the field.

"Now, grow, damn you, *grow!*" he shouted to the boll weevils he hoped were clinging to the roots. He made a rather lordly gesture across the acreage.

"Increase and multiply," he said.

When he came back to the car his face wore a serene look.

"It has been a good night's work," he announced. "I suppose you realize what I have done, Master Ridley." I knew that he had salvaged some of his humiliation with diseased Arkansas cotton. "I have just destroyed the economic future of Texas."

14.

"I've thought of something," he said to me one morning. "It's so simple, so obvious, so right, that I'm amazed we didn't think of it before."

I didn't ask what it was. I knew he would tell me anyway but by asking I might somehow seem to be endorsing one of his schemes.

"You're going to like this," he assured me. We were on the way to New Orleans where I was to interview a man named Anthony Ingolia who, I had found that night in Arkansas, was actually the first person Demara had impersonated.

"It's going to save you money. Lots of money. And it's going to make me money." I was curious. "How much, for example," Demara asked me, "are your doctor bills? How much will it cost you to have this new baby? The doctor's fee and the hospital fee."

The doctor would come to about $300 and the hospital charge, even with Blue Cross, would come to something like $100, I told him.

"Did you ever think of having your baby at home?" he asked.

I had thought about it. I had been born at home, for example. Everyone used to be born at home in the South, until the shortage of doctors during World War II caused doctors to insist that their patients report into hospitals.

"You can't get doctors to deliver babies at home anymore," I said.

"I know of an excellent doctor who will do that," Demara told me. "How would you like to save one hundred and fifty dollars on your doctor bill also?"

"Fine," I said. "But who's the doctor?"

"Me," he said.

I looked at him with blank astonishment.

"I'm going to be your doctor."

We talked about the proposal for most of that morning. He was excited and exuberant about the idea, and I could see that it meant something far more to him than merely serving as a doctor again, and he made me promise to call Judy that noon.

I explained the proposal to her as well and as carefully as possible. I covered the ground that Demara had had extensive experience delivering babies, since part of his job was delivering the wives of navy personnel. I also went on to the fact that he had performed major surgery while on the high seas, and because of that his experience in an emergency would be considerably beyond that of the average obstetrician.

"But he doesn't have a license to practice," Judy said.

"He didn't have a license *then*."

"Yes, but I have a good doctor now. I'm perfectly happy with Dr. Monroe."

"Monroe is a good doctor," I agreed. "He also is an expensive doctor."

"You wouldn't risk your child for the sake of a few pennies?"

"No, no, it isn't like that. You know that. It's just that, well, it *means* so much to him."

He was looking in through the glass partition of the telephone booth at me giving me the V-for-victory sign. I kept smiling back at him as best as I could.

"Well it *means* so much to me, too," she said.

We paused for a full half-minute of long-distance, expensive silence.

"Bob, you tell him this for me. Say how much I appreciate his offer but that I couldn't possibly leave Dr. Monroe at this point of the game. Tell him it would be unethical."

"*That's* a good one," I said. "That's a hot one, in fact."

"Well, just tell him that I don't need him. You've got to do that. Don't put it off the way you do. It'll only lead to trouble. Promise me."

"I promise."

When I came out of the booth his face was so glowing with happiness and excitement, his whole being was so exuberant and filled with expectation, I could barely make myself look at him.

"Well, what did my little patient have to say?" he boomed.

"She—she said she'd think it over," I said, and sidled away.

"That means she's sold," Demara said.

15.

Money was by now a serious problem but I was the only one who knew it. The advance on the book had been devoured and I was now dipping, although skimming was more like it, into the shallow capital in my bank account. It was now only a matter of time until Judy would cash a check and find that the account was empty. I was hoping that it would be Judy since it would not be good to have a check bounce with the impostor along. As I figured it, we could either continue to stay in motels or eat, but we could not do both and expect to reach home. Besides telling the impostor that we did not need him as a doctor, I now had to ask him which he would rather do: go hungry or bed on the ground.

We were driving through a little Louisiana town on the road to New Orleans when our car was stopped by a Catholic priest. He came out onto the highway and held up his hand and then the doors of his church opened. First there came a file of boys and girls all holding palm fronds, and after that, filing through the row of fronds, came little boys and girls who were just coming from their First

Communion. After them came their parents, looking old and corrupt against such youth.

"Oh, this beautiful, blissful innocence," Demara sighed. "Can you believe such innocence can still exist? What happens to us?"

When we were allowed to move again, Demara kept turning around until the little band of temporary saints was out of sight.

"That's the life I miss above all," he said. "A dealer in innocence."

We talked after that about the role of the priest in the confessional and the power a priest possesses to send people spotless into the world.

"Now you've got something. That's the secret secret of the Church," Demara said. "It's the one thing Freud and all the analysts can't do; remove guilt and restore innocence. The Church can."

I no longer wondered why he was so attracted to the Church. It was the old questing after the grail of innocence.

Years before, he told me, he had had his first real religious experience in Louisiana. He had been in the army, after three years in a monastery, and was on his way to New Orleans when he felt a terrible need to say a Mass. He stopped in a small town and told a local priest that he was a priest serving in the army and was able to sufficiently persuade the priest to let him say Mass. He felt inspired, but the experience also troubled him for years after.

Below the town of Dixie, on the highway to Shreveport,

following the flow of the Red River, we began meeting
signs announcing an old-time revival camp meeting. I
knew it was a bad day to start seeing those signs since I
was eager to get to New Orleans. I was hoping Demara
was missing them but by the glitter in his eyes I knew he
wasn't.

YOU'D TAKE A BATH TO GO TO THE
DANCE
HOW ABOUT GETTING WASHED FOR
JESUS?

Cowboy Tolliver

The minister running the revival was the Reverend
T. Texas Tolliver, but we soon learned that the real star
of the show was Cowgirl Candy Kane.

COTTON UP TO CHRIST
WITH CANDY KANE!

It was still light when we reached the tent, an orange
canvas affair with rolled-up walls that reeked of candied
apples and popcorn balls and old carny days. The
service was not due to begin until seven o'clock but the
makeshift parking lot was filled with clay-covered cars,
pickup trucks and even a few mule-drawn wagons.

HEAR BILLY-JOE SUGGS PLAY
"THAT OL' RUGGED CROSS" ON
THE $1,000 ELECTRIC GUITAR

I did my best to get by, talking loudly and insistently
about the political face of the nation, but it didn't work.

"*Stop!*" he ordered. He fixed me with an accusing look. "You know me better than *that*," he said. "We *couldn't* pass this by. You know that."

We parked the car and waded through the dust of the fields to the tent. It was nearly filled when we got in. It was a strange blend of the old and the new and, from previous experience, I expected there to be a mixture of Negro and white. The tent was lit by kerosene lamps hanging from the ridgepole, although the Rev. Tolliver's pulpit, white and glittering with silver stars and red bicycle reflectors, was lit by a row of lights whose power was supplied by a parked jeep outside.

Mr. Suggs was strumming low on his expensive instrument and a local jack-leg preacher, an amateur warm-up speaker, was trying to bring the crowd around for the arrival of the important preachers. The church was segregated, men on the right, women on the left and no Negroes at all. This was a wise precaution since there is nothing quite like a hell-fire rouser to cause men and women to leap into each other's embrace. The "pews" were perhaps the most primitive part of the church, being nothing but rough-hewn two-by-fours stretched out across orange crates and saw horses.

I didn't know, but I could sense it wasn't a good night. The crowd was not coming around, and to make things worse T. Texas Tolliver's voice had shouted itself into a barely audible whisper. Unable to carry the load he was forced to turn the meeting over to Billy-Joe who twanged into a few rocking, rollicking religious hymns that at least got the sinners swaying, a few feet stamping, hands clapping and one old man banging a tambourine on the side of his head as if he were helping beat the devil out of his brains. And then Sister Candy Kane came on.

She was dressed entirely in white. She wore a white cowboy hat that glittered with silver dust which had been sprinkled on it, and her white leather jacket and skirt tinkled with silver buttons. She wore white cowboy boots and held in her hand a long, white plastic staff topped by a silver cross. Candy Kane was eight years old.

"How y'all?" she said, smiling at all the people in the church. "Ready to come n' git saved with me tonight?"

"You bet we are," one powerful, raw-looking oil worker boomed, and everyone smiled.

"I'm so tiny, and I've done *such* terrible thangs," she began, and then she began to run down the list of awful things she had done and the horrors of her life up till then. The worst crime that I can recall was when she kept the dime her mother had given her to put in the church collection.

"Oh, that was mean and nasty," the Rev. Tolliver shouted. "Ol' devil workin' double-duty *that* day."

Billy-Joe strummed a low, dirty blues note. The audience cried, "Amen."

"Know what ah did?" she asked. "I spent that dahm on the jaw breakers and I wishet I was daid. Yes, I wishet I was daid, choked to death on them jaw breakers. I wishet . . ."

Demara nudged me, nearly knocking me off my perch.

"These aren't *sins*," he growled. "Christ, I'll show them some *real* sins."

My heart began to thump in the fashion it now was doing all the time.

"Yes, I wishet I was underneath the ground. I wishet my mommy would shovel clay on my little haid. Oh, I wishet . . ."

"They're going to learn about *big* sin," he said. "Go and get that truck horn," he commanded.

The truck horn was a large, three-toned, old-fashioned manually operated air horn I had found on an old truck in an auto graveyard and which I was bringing home for my children. Two of the notes no longer worked but the third did. It had a great, sad, bellowing honk to it and reminded me, when I first heard it sound, of a giant goose being disemboweled; tragic, protesting, and always behind it, the faint, far sound of doomsday.

A few young children, some of them decked out in cowboy and cowgirl suits, came forward to be witnesses to their future salvation, and then the little towhead sweetheart savior came down among the rough-hewn country sinners and touched their red, hurt, hard hands with her little white ones as if virtue were being instilled.

"Now, you be good and I'll be good, you hear?" she said, and then passed out of the tent into a trailer parked outside and into her trundle bed. I estimated that there was at least ten dollars in silver dumped in Candy Kane's hat.

I watched the Rev. Tolliver, massaging his throat, struggle to his feet again, reluctant to storm the bastions of hell that night, when I became conscious that Demara had left me and was moving through the sawdust.

He has many things in his favor. For one thing, he looks

like a preacher. As he started up that sawdust trail, drag-
ging his horn behind him, he exuded a sense of control.
Tolliver began to wave him back but Demara merely
nodded his head in that manner that says don't worry
about me, everything's going to be fine, and then he
mounted the shouter's stump. He put the horn down by
his right foot.

He took off his coat, every gesture slow and almost painful. His eyes seemed deep and lost inside him. He folded
one of the coat sleeves so slowly that the audience almost
moved with the fold, and then he did the second sleeve
and finally, while every eye stared at his broad back in
some bewilderment, he put down the coat *just so,* moving
it an inch one way and an inch another way.

"What's *his* song," Mr. Suggs called over to me. His
song was actually the Gregorian plain chants, but that
didn't seem right for a Louisiana tent meeting. I asked
him to try one of my favorites, "Rock Me In Thy Bosom,"
and he gave me a queer look.

"That's a nigger song," he said, with no apparent malice, and then I recalled Demara's favorite from Maine
where he had run a Baptist Sunday school.

"Give him 'Jesus, Take Me for a Sunbeam,' " I said. It
isn't good camp meeting music but Billy-Joe gave it a
rocking country ride and it passed. I could sense that the
impostor was pleased.

When the last fold of the coat had been made, and the
audience was firmly in his hands, he whirled.

"You're all frauds!" he cried. "You're fakes! Every single one of you is an *impostor.*"

There was a gasp from the people. I suspicioned that they didn't know what an impostor was but they had the feeling it was worse than being a common sinner. He was bent over as if he were about to charge into them, and his voice rose in volume with each sentence.

"You people think you come as sinners.

"Yes, you think you come in shame."

      "That's right, that's right," they began saying.

"You think you know of evil

"Yeah, you think you know of the devil."

                    "We do, we do."

Demara began to sway imperceptibly to the left and right and some of the people, reaching out to him now, were swaying, too. Billy-Joe Suggs was thumping his guitar in time with the sway and together, the low, persistent music and the chanting voice, was getting to the people.

"Yes, you all think you act so mean."

                    "That's right."

"And feel so mean."

                    "You're right."

"And talk so mean."

                    "That's right."

"And think so mean."

                    "You're right."

Somebody slapped my notebook out of my hand. "Stop that writin', them's God's words you're writin'." I picked up the notebook out of the oily sawdust and put my pencil away. He kept chanting for perhaps another several minutes. I had no feeling of time but as cynical as I was, the pull of the chant and of the people around me was hard to resist. His device was the same, but he changed the words, from mean to rotten and sick and shameful and sinful and the litany would be repeated with each new embellishment. He had them all swaying when he suddenly ceased to talk.

"But you blind me!" he suddenly shouted, breaking the line of the chant. He clapped his hands over his eyes with a stinging smack of the flesh.

"Compared to me . . . compared to my blackness . . . compared to this sinner"—he thumped his chest—"your souls are shining so white I can't see you.

"You look like little children.

"Yes, you come . . .

"Pure as the driven snow."

He began to pick up the quality of the chant again and the people swung in with it, instinctively changing their response now to *Amen.*

"Bright like the morning sun."

"Amen."

"Fresh as the first frost."

"Amen."

"Innocent as the baby lamb."

"Amen."

"White as the wings of the dove."

"Amen."

And then he began to use the local images and the people felt it deeper.

"Yes, clean as new cotton."

"Amen."

"Right as spring rain."

"Amen."

"Sound as good sorghum."

"Amen."

"Happy as money."

"Amen."

The people were moved. Usually their lot was to be told what sinners they were and then how they were going to burn and be tortured for it, but Demara was doing it differently. He stopped again.

"But, don't you ever forget . . ."

Eeeee-wonk! He mashed his foot down on the rubber bulb of the truck horn and the scream of the dying goose shattered the stillness of the tent.

"You're going to die the death!"

The congregation nearly erupted as a unit off the hard planks and hand-hewn pine logs. I felt my heart leap and begin pounding. Some people cried out and others sat stunned.

"You remember," Demara shouted above the turmoil. "Everybody goes when that wagon comes!"

Eeeeeeeee-wonk!

"No, don't you forget it! When Death comes knocking, you got to open the door."

Eeeeeee-wonk!

"Yes, you do. When the Boatman comes, you got to climb on board."

Eeeeeeee-wonk!

Candy Kane, roused by the scream of the goose, had come from the trailer and was standing in a side entrance to the tent with what I took to be her parents. The Rev. Tolliver was as caught up as the rest of the congregation. I had a feeling he was going to start pounding his head against the plank his brow rested on. A country woman wearing men's farm boots began to holler in a scary way, and when she began to get a fit of stiff jerks, as if she were seized, several of the women had to hold her and then help her down the aisle. I looked back then to the impostor and he seemed seized himself. His eyes had a "gone away" appearance and his face looked like I had never seen it look, intense and yet calm, forceful and yet gentle.

He kept it up until it was almost too much. Some of the younger people, less hardened to camp meetings, had ceased to react and merely sat crying. A great many of the people were on the verge of undergoing some kind of emotional and even physical seizure. I remember one near the end that struck me as particularly good:

"The end of the line is the Land of the Dead, and *Everyman* owns a passport."

And then the cry of the goose, the last, sad, haunting honks. He squeezed the rubber bulb three times.

Eeee-wonk

Eeeeeeee-wonk

Eeeeeeeeee-wonk
trumpeted for the last time.

After that he began to tell them very quietly what a sinner he was, and they believed him.

"Oh, you *were* terrible," a woman sang out over and over.

"You were the worst, oh, you were the worst," the people reassured him, as he lined out his sins. He spoke directly about some of his actual impostorings. He told how he had maltreated some of their own sons in the Texas prison system. I don't know if anyone understood what he was telling them, but they understood his need to tell them.

Toward the very end, while he was crying and the people were sobbing with him, he managed a line that might set a high water mark for tent evangelism.

"If that Red River outside this tent flows until Judgement Day, it won't match the tears of blood my people have shed for the sinful life I've led."

When he finished and came down off the stump, the people applauded him, something I have learned is almost never done. They recognized quality.

"Oh, didn't he preach, didn't that man *preach?*" I heard.

As he came down among them, the truck horn still at the ready the way I always picture Gabriel to be, they felt a need to get around him. He wore a beatific, rested smile while looking and nodding at everyone, but he didn't hear or see them. We gently pushed our way to the tent flaps.

"That fat preacher, wasn't he grand?" a woman said to me.

"That man ought to be a Baptist bishop."

"He will, he will," I assured her.

I saw Sister Candy Kane peeking at us from the shuttered window of her trailer, her face sallow against the
dead white of her clothes, sick with envy.

She looked like the devil.

In the car later that night I witnessed that look of con-
tentment gradually sink into one of dumbness. The impostor was drained; that which had supported him was
spent. He had sat upright with the air horn by his side
and each time a car came toward us I had been able to
watch his face in the momentary splash of light. Gradually
I had the feeling that his personality had left his body,
the mind and soul were gone, only the flesh remained
behind.

"Now you know everything," he mumbled once to me.
Much later he said: "I really believe all that. That's my
trouble. I won't tomorrow."

Later he fell asleep, and when I stopped for gas I took
the horn away and put it back in the trunk. But sometime
after that, on an impulse, I stopped the car out along
the highway and took the horn out of the trunk and
carried it over to the drainage ditch that paralleled the
road. It sank in the lily pads. I never wanted to hear
that lonesome sound again.

We got to New Orleans in the deep dead of night and
somehow I got the impostor into a motel with the aid of
a young Negro boy who was taking the night watch and
who asked me if I was sure that Demara were alive.

In the morning he woke "sober as a Jesuit, as solemn as
a hymn." It was as if nothing had happened. He never
noticed the horn was missing.

We spent that morning looking for Anthony Ingolia, the first man Demara had impersonated, but we didn't try very hard. I wanted to get home and Demara didn't seem to have much zest for experience.

"I liked that line, 'Everybody goes when that wagon comes,' best of all," I said.

"What line?" he asked me. I told him and he was only vaguely conscious of the entire performance. He seemed to feel guilty about it, as if he had done something sacrilegious, but he recalled no details. I quoted some of the other lines I remembered, and he was both amazed and embarrassed at them.

"Those are Southern things, those aren't mine."

I noticed him shudder faintly, as if he were trying to shrug off a mantle that was annoying him. "I don't think like that and I don't talk like that."

I know that at times Demara has been haunted with the idea that his body becomes possessed by spirits or forces other than his own. He feels that part of this comes from the confusion of all his identities but part of it is something that he can't account for or explain. He asked me, for the first time, to read some of the things I had managed to get down and while I did I noticed him struggling, I feel, to identify who was talking through him.

"I don't like the son of a bitch," he suddenly said. And that was the end of the affair; we never said another word about it.

In New Orleans we made the big turn. It was the end of the journey out and the start of the voyage in. It made a remarkable change in our attitudes. Now we had a goal and plans and responsibilities. That night, before the early morning start, Demara, in a wave of new enthusiasm, sat down and wrote a long and careful letter to my wife.

He kept mentioning the subjects to me as he went along; problems of diet, low-salt diets if any edema showed, theories about breathing exercises and other obstetrical lore he harbored.

That was when I had to tell him the truth. I kept trying but each time I felt it was the proper time he put me off with another surge of enthusiasm about the whole idea.

"Any patient of mine is entitled to the utmost consideration," he said, professorially. "Will you please mail this?"

He handed me the letter and I took it down to the lobby to get an airmail stamp. I didn't want to open that letter. I know that criminals often say that; they didn't mean to do it, but they found themselves doing it. Always against their wills. Children are masters at this. So I have no legitimate excuse or one I can ask you to believe but I feel kinder now to certain criminals than I did before. I found my fingers moving faster than I could control them, feeling the gummed paper, cutting away at it and extracting the letter.

To my very dear, unknown patient:

I realize that this is a highly unusual way to meet your doctor but for those of us who have had experience in the wilds of Canada it actually isn't. To put you at your ease, let me tell you a story of how I helped deliver a score of babies over the telephone and over radio and then consider that I will be dealing with you personally within the week. . . .

I read the rest of it, all of it, and I was mortified doing it. There were highly complimentary things in the letter about me telling Judy what a patient and enduring traveling companion I was and what a fine person I was and a variety of subjects revolving about his upcoming case.

I tore the letter up and put it in a wastebasket in the lobby and then, like a common thief, I was afraid that he might spot the pieces so took them out of the basket and out onto the street and dumped them down a sewage drain. After that I walked around for a long time, since I didn't have the nerve to go back up to the room and look him in the face. I knew he could read me like I read his letter.

16.

The car died in Nashville.

It died at five o'clock in the afternoon, at the beginning of rush hour. The car had slowed to make a difficult left turn across three lanes of onrushing traffic when it died. It was hard to believe that this motor, which only a moment before had been pulsing with life, was now stilled.

"*I'm* not going to push the goddamn thing," Demara said.

It had not gone out without a fight, I could say that for it. The engine had coughed and fought for life, and, several times even after it seemed certain the car was dead, it lurched a few feet forward in almost convulsive twitches. The car had moved just enough to now block one and one-half lanes of traffic.

"I don't expect *you* to push it," I said. "You drive and I'll try to push it."

The cars seemed to press down on our exposed flank like a herd of buffalo preparing to stampede.

"I have humiliated myself for the last time," he said. "This is *your* mess. Get out of it *your* way."

I tried hard to breathe a spark of life back into the car

by frantically turning on the key and working every trick
I had had to master over the years, but it was very clear
that this time, after so many false alarms, the Death
Wagon was done for.

"I have strained myself," he shouted at me, since the
din of automobile horns had now reached an almost
shattering decibel, "I have ruptured myself, I have risked
strokes, I have disgraced myself. This is it. I am through."

"Get this heap out of here," the policeman yelled
through Demara's window.

"Not *my* car," the impostor said, calmly folding his
arms.

"Officer," I said, "I am willing to push if he'll only—"

"You shut up!" the policeman said. He turned back to
Demara. "Now, you. Get out and push."

Demara turned on me.

"If I wasn't what I am, I wouldn't be doing this and
don't you forget it."

He got out of the car.

"My God, he's as big as a bull," the policeman said.
"Come on, put some beef in it."

If Demara had had the gun I had dropped in the Red
River, he would have killed that man. As it was he turned
an amazing color of red and veins I had never seen before
stood out on his forehead.

We were unfortunately on a slight incline not in our
favor. I could not have moved the car, but, with Demara
pushing, it slowly inched ahead, picking up speed.

It will stand as one of the low marks in the impostor's
career. In full view of a hostile audience that was beginning to number in the hundreds, prodded by a lowly

traffic cop, under the stares, the horns and the hoots of the mob, he pushed his shameful burden, the ancient Death Wagon, across the highway to its grave.

He came back to the window on my side of the car.

"Fred, you know I—" I tried to apologize, but he would not have it.

"This is the end, that's all. The end."

He took a few things from the back of the car and started walking down the road toward Nashville. I started after him but I finally had to stop. Everything we owned was lying exposed in the car. I ran back to it and piled everything in the trunk and locked the car up as best as I could. Then I began running. I ran until I could run no more and finally managed to hitch a ride into town, as Demara must have done.

A few weeks before I would have been in a panic but now I had the confidence of knowing my man. I telephoned my cousin Bob who lives in Nashville and asked him the name of the best hotel in the city. I went to it and asked for the room of Mr. Ben W. Jones.

Demara had many times mentioned the fact that Mr. O. B. Ellis of the Texas prison system was originally from Nashville. I knew my man well enough to know by now that Demara's idea of irony would be to check in under the name of the man who had defrauded Ellis.

The impostor was aghast when he answered the door. For the first time I witnessed him robbed of any semblance of poise. And then, quite unexpectedly, a great smile broke over his face.

"Marvelous," he said. "You've done it." He clapped me

on the shoulders with unrestrained admiration. "You have got inside the mind of the great impostor."

It called for a celebration.

I felt that a certain real barrier that had always existed between us had broken down. It was really the first time he had ever acknowledged any quality on my part except endurance, which I feel he took for stupidity and which, I suspect, often was.

"We'll go out on a toot tonight," he said, and right then I informed him that we were almost out of money.

"All right," he said affably, "I can bear it. We'll just have to good soldier it all the way home. I can live on nothing, you know. That's *another* of my secrets. I've been a Trappist."

While I got a taxi and went out to the highway and got all of our things Demara got a few good bottles of bourbon. He had done justice to one of them by the time I returned.

It had been a long day. As early as ten o'clock that morning, on a dare from me, Demara had made a speech in favor of integration in Jackson, Mississippi. The dare had begun during the course of an argument in which he had insisted that if anything were done with charm it would be acceptable in any quarter. I then challenged Demara to make a speech in favor of integrated schools and mixed marriages in the very heartland of dedicated segregation. It was a thing I shouldn't have done.

In a downtown public park in Jackson, near the market section, at the base of a statue raised in the memory of the boys and men who had died for the Confederate States of

America, Demara delivered a speech in favor of integrating the races in Mississippi. I don't recall any specific statement he made. The audience was composed largely of loafers and public park loungers with a sprinkling of people passing through, and I spent almost every moment looking up the concrete paths for signs of an approaching policeman. It was part of the deal that if the police came Demara would talk on. I never warned him that a policeman was coming but a moment before a city patrolman ambled into sight Demara had closed with his plea that the schools in Jackson would soon be filled equally with white and colored children so that future inter-marriage would occur on a natural, familiar basis.

"I don't like *what* the man says, but I like the *way* he says it," a man said to me at the fringe of the small crowd. By the time the policeman had pieced together exactly what had taken place in his park we were moving fast through the tropical greenery and were gone. The Death Wagon, as if sensing the urgency of the situation, responded at once.

Then, later, I had placed a call from Yazoo City to New York from an open, public telephone screwed to a pillar in the middle of a lunch room. The long-distance call alone was enough to arouse curiosity among the local people present and when I reached Judy, both of us shouting on the phone as is our habit when the distance of the call is over a few miles, she informed me that a Negro family had moved in next door to us.

"They seem to be awfully nice," Judy shouted. "And there's a little boy. Thank God, Robby will have another boy to play with."

What could I say? I felt the eyes of some of Yazoo City's Citizen Council members burning holes through me. What was it they did to my kind; tarred and feathered them or horsewhipped them through the street. If I knew Demara he would manage somehow to be at the head of the pack. However, before I felt the hairy touch of the rope, the conversation changed.

"How did he take it?" Judy asked me.

"Take what?"

"Your telling him I didn't want him to be my doctor."

"Oh, that. Oh, he took it all right," I said. She can always tell.

"You're lying," she said. "I can tell you're lying. You never told him. Oh, Bob, this is getting serious. You've got to tell him."

"How can you say things like that?" I shouted, and hung up in a complete fluster of embarrassment.

"My, my, what were you so mad about?" Demara asked me in the car.

"Oh, nothing," I said.

"Something about me, wasn't it?"

"No," I shouted at him. It had wrecked the day.

Now the car was dead, we were broke and I saw no way out but to drink. It seemed to help Demara mightily. After a few stiff hookers of Jack Daniel's best Tennessee sour mash whisky I had the nerve to call Nashville Bob and borrow money to buy two railroad tickets to New York. The arrangement to get the money, as befits my cousin, was very odd and pleased Demara no end. I was told to take a taxi to an address which turned out to be a back-alley warehouse. While I stumbled about in semi-black-

ness, a door opened in a huge shed and we were waved in
by a man I barely saw and certainly didn't know.
We were led along a path that wound between towering
piles of huge truck and heavy-equipment tires, down some
winding stairs, through a black hall lit dimly by one bulb
and then through a door that seemed, at first glance, to
lead to nothing. This was Hollywood stuff all the way.

Inside of the door was the private entity of Nashville
Bob named, with a rather lamentable lack of imagination, Hernando's Hideaway. There stood a solid, ample
well-stocked bar, a complete, tidy kitchen, a slick, compact
dining room and three or four bedrooms, one of which
held the chef-bartender. A man might hide in there away
from bombs or the law or his wife for years. I will not
hazard which one my cousin was then fleeing from.

A set up such as the Hideaway is, naturally, one of
Demara's ultimate dreams, and he was furious when I
wouldn't let him stay the night. I felt the company was
too fast, and we were led, bumping and bouncing along
the rubbery trail, back to the unromantic hotel.

"Look at your cousin. A man hiring hundreds of people,
a man of taste, and what are you? A lousy notetaker."

He got my orange notebook out of the pocket of my
coat on a chair and began doing a ponderous, thunderous
waltz around the room.

"A literary peeping Tom," he said. "An unen-
lightened, unembarrassed eavesdropper." I was too tired
to fight back.

"I will bet you that I can make a bird fly away with this
notebook," he said.

What was there to say to this nonsense except to suspect that Demara, under the divine guidance of Jack Daniel's, was entering a St. Francis phase.

"You have power over birds," I said with heavy sarcasm. "You have daily chats with them, is that it?"

"I am deadly in earnest," he said. "If the birds fly away with your book, will you let me read it?"

"If the birdies fly back with it again, yes," I said.

"And if they don't, I'll never mention the book again. Agreed?"

"Agreed," I said. I was too tired to grasp his outstretched hand. It was around five thirty in the morning, an hour or two after I had gone to sleep, when he wakened me.

"The birds have come," he whispered in my ear.

I tried to get out of bed but I was too weak. On the window sill I could see the notebook lying with perhaps one-third of its length projecting over the ledge. Even from where I was, I could see that the cover of the book had been coated with some syrupy substance and that in the syrup, sticking to it, were corn flakes and pop corn and pieces of crushed peanuts.

One of them was already there and then the rest came: noxious balls of plumed puffs, pigeons—ten of them and then twenty of them, a slate-gray cloud of them, with their little etched pebbles for eyes, their pink feet dancing desperately to keep a hold on the sill, and their wings fluttering wildly to keep their balance. I finally found the strength to get out of bed and go for the window but he stopped me. While I struggled to get around him I kept crying, "Unfair, unfair," and then it was too late.

When I reached the window, they were gone, down,

down into the gloom, dropping swiftly with the orange-covered book whose leaves fluttered as wildly as the wings of a wounded dove, and then the birds and the book dropped into black obscurity. Away off I could see morning coming. The sky was clear and bright, a good day, although down in the back alley it was still night.

I turned back to look at Demara.

"It was an act of God," he said. "Our feathered friends have come, and our feathered friends have flown." He yawned hugely while I put on my shoes and started after the notebook.

"The Lord giveth, and the Lord taketh away."

"You are a filthy, sick, immoral man," I said. He smiled sweetly.

"Did I *tell* you anything but that?"

It stopped me since it was true. He had spent weeks trying to convince me of just that.

"I don't know why you're so eager to rush out and get the thing. I've got first lookies."

It was something I would have to risk. When he saw the book he would leave me, and there were too many facts still to be revealed. Yet without it, I felt I would be lost. I hoped I might be able to edit and censor the notes in some form before he could study the worst of what I had written. It only occurs to me now that I might easily have pocketed the book and claimed not to have found it.

"Do you know Emily Dickinson?"

"Of course, I know Emily Dickinson," I said.

"Oh," he said softly, "then you'll remember this:

> *"God gave a loaf to every bird*
> *But just a crumb to me."*

He began laughing. I could hear the quality of that laugh all the way down the hall and while I waited for the elevator to reach me. It enraged me. I went back down the hall.

"You are truly beginning to irritate me," I said to him from the door. He stopped laughing and fixed me with a hard look.

"Look, Crichton. I'm not that fond of you myself. Your trouble is, you're stuck with me. I can go any time I choose."

It was all too terribly true.

"The only single reason I'm still sticking with you is to help your wife have that baby."

I closed the door quietly and stood in the hall and felt like someone had just pierced my soul with an icicle.

17.

The orange notebook was never found. I searched all that morning for it, crawling through a parking lot looking under cars, and even scaling a wall onto the roof of a small restaurant which was within flying distance of the hotel room. Even Demara helped. Whenever he saw a cluster of pigeons he shooed them aside in the hope of finding a flash of orange beneath them. We searched until it was time to get the train. In some ways I was relieved, since I had lived in dread for weeks that Demara would some-day read some of the things I had written about him. It is a credit to his personal honesty and self-discipline that he never opened the jacket of the book, although it teased him unmercifully.

I hadn't been on a railroad train in a long time and we talked about the feeling of tradition and solid assurance that a train has.

"They really go clackety-clack," Demara said. I told him how I still recall with horror a poem I wrote to one of my first real loves when I was on my way back to prep school.

> *Clackety-clack, clackety-clack*
> *Sing the wheels against the track*
> *And every clack*
> *Sings you won't be back.*
> *Alack!*

I never saw the girl after that.

But even the feeling of going home at last, the feeling of having a little money, and the reassuring rocking along of the train no longer worked. Each clackety-clack in this case began to fill me with dread. I had to find some way to break the awful news about Judy and the baby. As the days went on our conversation more and more turned to the subject. Since several of our recent blowups it became one of the few safe things to talk about although I found it harder and harder to sound enthusiastic.

The trouble now was that I was in too deep. I had let things go entirely too long and too far and I could find no formula for backing down. Beyond badly hurting Demara's feelings, which I was bound to do, was a second consideration. He could, on the basis of this, become a committed enemy. He could ruin the entire project in a way that he had only recently begun reminding me about. It was written in our contract that Demara would have final approval of the book. He had once said to me in a teasing way: "What if I don't like the opening sentence?"

"I'd write another," I said.

"Yes, but I wouldn't like that one either. Or the next, or the next. What then?"

I had never answered him. There was no answer. But all that night I had dreamed that I was standing at a blackboard writing sentences over and over while the teacher kept erasing them. And I thought of the character in Camus' *The Plague* who spent thirty years writing the opening sentence to his book, and I got sick thinking about him.

There was one thing that cheered me. The impostor had taken to reading in *Why You Do What You Do.* Whenever possible I studied his face for any reaction. He seemed to be enormously absorbed by what he found there. God knows what a flood of ideas and thoughts might be released by his reading.

We were in the club car and he was drinking and I was trying to anesthetize my fears by drinking, a thing that was happening a good deal those days, when we witnessed the longest double-take in the history of the Louisville and Nashville Railroad, if not in the western world.

A young man entered the club car and took a seat opposite us.

"Look." I nudged Demara. The man took out a copy of *Life* magazine which was now weeks old and in which there were pictures and a story about Demara's Maine caper. He ordered a beer and began flipping through the pages. It was only a matter of minutes until he came to the spot. If no one had moved he might very well have failed to notice that the impostor he was reading about was sitting four feet away. I questioned Fred with my eyes if he wanted to leave, but instead Demara made an enormous false sneeze causing the young man to look up and study him. Several times he made loud, vulgar noises and aimless statements. Each time the man glanced at him around the corner of the magazine or over the top.

It was evident when the proper page was reached.

The magazine was snapped apart with a *crack*. For a brief second he didn't move, then the man's head shot up over the top for one lightning fast look at the impostor across the aisle. And then it shot back down again.

For two nearly unbearable minutes the man made not another move. His legs, which had flashed out from beneath him when he had reacted to the picture, were as stiff as those of the dead. They never twitched. His fingers were frozen to the paper. There was no hint that he was breathing.

Then the magazine began to move down at the rate of possibly a quarter of an inch every two minutes. Down it came, a flick at a time, one desperate inch after another until we could finally see the top of his crew cut head, When the magazine was within an inch or two of eye level Demara got up from his seat and sneaked across the aisle until he was crouched at the man's feet. For a minute he was forced to wait that way—and finally the man dared to lower the magazine all the way.

For one horrible moment he found himself staring directly into the eyes of the dreaded master impostor. For that moment he remained as he had been. He was immobilized.

"That's right," Demara said, "it's *me*."

"Eeee-*yow*," the man cried. He flung the magazine into the air, clambered recklessly to his feet, and began running. I realize it is not possible but I have the clear recollection that he was down the club car and out of it before the magazine reached the floor.

Later that night I went back into the club car. Demara was reading *Why You Do What You Do* again, and after a few bourbons I dared to try him out on it.

"How's it going?" I tried.

"Splendid, really splendid."

"Learning anything?" I tried once more.

"Not a single thing," he said. "I'm learning that the fear of death, if you wait long enough for it, can warp men's minds. But then I always knew that."

It was several bourbons later that my solution came to me as clearly as a vision.

Get a new wife.

I had been forgetting that Demara had never met my wife. And that he had never seen my house. He knew the address, but that could be remedied.

Was it so implausible, so profoundly reckless that I should not rent or borrow a wife for the afternoon, a nice trim wife who had just given birth to a baby a few days before? The baby, of course, would have to be held at the hospital in an incubator under observation. All I would need was a woman, an apartment in my building if I couldn't get Judy to leave our own, and then salt and pepper the place with toys and family pictures. The other children, I would tell him, were away with their grand-parents in the country.

After all, the precedent for such doing had been well established. I would have an impostor wife.

I have rarely felt as elated as I was that night. "I only hope we're not too late," I said to Demara. "For what?"

"Why, for you to deliver the baby. She said she really felt imminent."

"Why the hell didn't you tell me that before," he demanded. He was furious.

"I felt it would only worry you," I said, unperturbed.

"We would have taken the plane, for God's sake. This is important." He lapsed into a prolonged period of brooding. I should have left well enough alone. When he wouldn't talk to me, I decided to prowl through the train and corral the young man Demara had terrified and explain how the impostor is really the gentle, lovable impostor. He wasn't to be found. I knew where his seat had been and I finally asked the conductor if he knew where the man might have gone, and he said he had gotten off at Columbus. His ticket, which he had left behind in the club car, had been marked through for Pittsburgh.

When I got back into the club car Demara was gone, but he had left *Why You Do What You Do* behind. I couldn't resist peeking to see which chapter he was then studying. I hoped it was one of the chapters in the section called "The Web of Neuroses." There also was a large white card or bookmark on which I had seen Demara writing something. I know that he hadn't looked at my orange notebook, but then I was the writer. I told myself I had a duty to read his notes.

The note read: "I don't know why you do what you do, but I do know who done it. The butler."

For a moment I didn't quite understand, but then I realized that the book inside the jacket cover was not the same book at all. It was a murder mystery written by Mignon Eberhart.

When I looked up again Demara was standing down at the far end of the club car, rolling a bottle of beer between his hands, smiling at me with the most satanic smile that ever has been directed at me.

"Made a little fool of yourself, didn't you?" he said loudly. The few people who were in the club car at that hour turned to look at me. I turned a deep, shameful red. I wished I could have been back with the other victim in Columbus right at that moment. That might have solved everything.

18.

The city seemed foreign and formidable that morning, as it always does to me on re-entering it. No one ever seems to know me or even to be liable to know me when I come back to this place. As always I felt a stranger in my home. Demara hates New York for that reason, but I refuse to give up hoping that someday I will feel at home here, the way I do in other cities after two weeks time.

He was annoyingly demanding about seeing Judy; he wanted to see her that moment. I was beginning to see that assisting at the birth of this baby had come to mean to Demara a whole justification for all the things he had told me, even a justification in some way for the things he had done. I also felt that it would give him the strength to remake a new image of himself.

My job now was to first get rid of Demara for that morning so that I could get to work on my own impostoring. Fortunately Nestingen's apartment was still available, and I had a place to put him. He went there only after I insisted Judy would not see him until she first had a few hours of privacy with me. He very reluctantly agreed.

Before even placing a call to her, I telephoned Upstairs Irma. Upstairs Irma was a young woman who lived
in the apartment one flight above us on Perry Street. If
I was going to pull this off I would need both her and her
apartment. First, however, I had to make certain both
were available. As I let the plot unfold, morsel after
juicy morsel, Upstairs Irma, as I suspected, was not only
willing to defraud the great defrauder, she was ravenous
for the role. She is what is known as "a good sport."

"Listen," she said. "I will play you such a new mother
whose babe is in the hospital that it will tear your very
heart out of your very body."

"There is such a thing as artistic economy," I cautioned.

"Tears?" she said. "You'll need a mop."

"Don't forget about overplaying," I suggested.

"I didn't play Camille in high school for like nothing,"
she said. "Oh, by the by, boy—" Irma used a good many
expressions like that—"what is it? A boy or girl?"

It was a good question. I decided we needed another
girl.

"Why don't we make it twins?" Irma suggested. "Then
I can *really* go to town."

There was this other thing about Upstairs Irma. If a
thing could be overdone, Irma very often was the girl to
give it a try.

I was beginning to appreciate the risks an impostor
must run.

I didn't call Judy but decided to surprise her instead.
I was fortunate in getting a taxi at Pennsylvania Station
and in a few minutes was dropped off at Perry Street. I
was home.

I opened the door quietly and went into the living room.

"I'm home," I said. For a moment I heard nothing and then I heard sounds from the kitchen and I looked into it. Sarah was making her favorite breakfast of rare bacon and tile eggs, eggs that had the consistency of bricks.

"Those eggs are too well done."

"We like them that way." She turned them over one by one. "Who are you?"

"I'm Daddy."

"I thought so." She didn't look up.

> *Home is the sailor, home from the sea,*
> *And the hunter home from the hill.*

"Didn't you really know?"

She thought for a moment. "Oh, yes, I knew. I knew when you opened the door. But I didn't want to say so."

"Did you miss me?"

"Yes," she said, but then she added. "And no. I mean at first we did and then we got used to it without you. Robbie doesn't know who you are any more. Mommie's asleep."

Sarah was very self-contained for just four.

It was astonishing how pregnant Judy was. It is always astonishing to see just how pregnant women do become. In the final weeks it always seems to be too much to be quite right. Despite the ordeal ahead of me with Demara I was glad now that Judy would not be alone when the baby came.

"I'm home."

"Thank God," she said. It was very rewarding.

A secret, if it is any good at all, is good enough to be kept a secret. I didn't *have* to tell her; I never should have. What she didn't know, she never needed to know.

I had made up my mind, so exuberant was I with my new plan, that the only way to handle it was to tell Judy straight out: No, I never did tell Demara you didn't want him for your doctor, even though he is counting desperately on it.

Speak straight out, and then, just when she was very low, spring the brilliant way out.

I honestly don't feel it would be fruitful or even decent for that matter, to go into how my wife received all this. She didn't receive any part of it. In a desperate reaction to her first response I simply told her the whole plan was just a passing thought, an amusing throwaway, and fell back on a second plan I had held all along. We might still find a way to keep the friendship of Demara and yet elude him as a doctor if I could find some way to stall him off until labor could be induced. We had tried it once before during an intolerable tropical heat wave. We had seen funny movies and taken bumpy car rides and drunk hot lemonade with syrup and it had seemed to work. This might have gone down with Judy, I don't know. But it would have to happen then.

"Isn't this the wildest?" It was Upstairs Irma on the phone. "I've already gotten the most cunning maternity bed jacket and I'm getting—"

"Irma," my wife said, "you can get out of your bed of pain and go to work. There isn't going to be a virgin birth." She turned back to me. "Just a little throw-away."

As I have said, I don't think it would be decent to go into any detail of what followed after that. I did my best to defend myself, however, on the grounds that I was mainly only trying to salvage the project.

"It's gone way beyond that," she told me. "The thing is not to salvage the project. The thing now is to salvage yourself."

And this was true. The book never need be written. The world was not going to be the sadder or lesser for that. The money Demara and I had already squandered would be a terrible blow but that might eventually be surmounted. But my own self-esteem or respect or pride, whatever it was, if I couldn't go face Demara and tell him the simple truth, if I couldn't be truthful with the man whose life I was going to spend a year of my own life writing, then what could be salvaged later for me?

I knew one thing. If I didn't come back home with the whole truth told, I would never be able to come home in the same way ever after.

"Ah, you're still there," I said, when he answered the phone in Nestingen's apartment.

"You're damn right I'm still here. Where do you think I'd be? I know where I want to be. I want to be down there with my patient. Put Judy on the phone."

"Fred, I think you'd better stay right there," I said.

"Play the man, Master Ridley, play the man."
It was all that I could hang onto all the way up to

the Beaux Arts Apartments. I said it over and over in
a kind of liturgical chant in the hope that it might keep
me from thinking about what lay ahead.

When I walked into the apartment, I found him
stretched out on an easy chair, his feet up on a window sill,
looking out over the East River. He was eating cheese on
crackers and sipping a glass of good Burgundy. On his lap
he held a medical book and down by the side of his chair
were three or four other medical books, all brand new.

"They are doing wonderful new things in obstetrics," he
said, without looking up.

I found I couldn't speak.

"The trouble with American doctors is that they don't
get a chance to keep up with their reading or research.
They stop the day they leave medical school."

He tapped the books by him.

"Got to keep hitting these. I will bet you right now that
I know more about obstetrical technique than any doctors in New York except the ones who are teaching it."

I was sinking, that was the only description of it. Everything in me was becoming depressed and squeezed, the
way I have read happens to astronauts when the pull
of gravity is defied. He had gotten up and gone to the icebox to get more cheese and pour another glass of wine.

"What's the matter with you?" he said. I didn't answer
him. He picked up the books and hefted them in his
hands and began reading me some of the impressive
sounding titles.

"They cost a lot of money but they're worth it," he
said. "Oh, well, I'll make it back out of the fee."

"There isn't going to be any fee," I heard myself say.
"What was that?"
I didn't know if I could bring myself to say it once more.
"There isn't going to be any fee."
He looked back over the top of his chair at me in a quizzical way. "You mean because you're broke?" I shook my head no.
"Meaning what?"
"Meaning I don't want you to deliver my wife's baby."
I felt at that moment unbearably sad and unbearably happy. For a long time he didn't move. I tried to lose myself in watching the intricate maneuvers of a string of barges attempting to get around an anchored freighter out in the river. When he did move, he moved very fast. He went past me so fast that I didn't see his face but that might have been because I didn't want to. He went into the little bedroom off the living room. I could hear him moving in the room, swiftly at something.
"Your wife feel the same way?" His voice sounded controlled and even reasonably happy.
"The same way."
"Didn't trust me, I guess?"
"It wasn't that. She had her own doctor."
He came to the door. All of the buoyancy of only a few minutes before was gone. He physically looked much smaller, a trait that I had come to expect in him.
"She didn't trust me."
When he came out in the hall he had, as I had feared, all of his luggage with him.

"When did you decide all this?" It would have been so easy to lie and say that morning. Perhaps I should have.

"Almost from the start." He nodded, as if listening to a patient detail his symptoms.

"And my letter?"

"I never mailed it. I tore it up."

My eyes were now riveted to the pile of medical books. I wanted to say that I would pay for them since they were my fault but I was afraid to mention them. Demara finished his wine, swept up the cracker crumbs and took a swift tour of the apartment to see if anything had been left behind.

"It all makes me ridiculous, doesn't it?" he said. He went into the bathroom and came back with a few toilet articles he had left.

"And what is the one thing in the world that I can't stand being made?"

"Ridiculous," I dutifully said.

"You've learned so many lessons so well," he said. "So late," he added.

He piled all the baggage by the door.

"It all started out so fine and it ended so rotten."

"Well, it was all my fault—"

"No," he cut in, "it just always does." He looked defeated and I hated to see that sadness that came into his eyes at those times. He had his hand on the door, but he came back across the room. He picked up the medical books and piled them in my arms.

"I won't be needing these. Give them to your doctor. He probably does. Oh, yes." He went into the bedroom and came out and put a last book on top of the pile of other books.

"You need this as much as I do."

It was *Why You Do What You Do.*

I watched him as far as the elevator and when it came and the door opened I waved and said good-by but he never turned to look at me.

I had done my duty. I had played the man. I had lived up to the requirements expected of Master Ridley. And yet I had never felt so shameful and childish.

19.

I guess I have never been so consistently depressed in my life as I was the week after Demara had gone. I spent the time trying to bring some order out of the mass of notes I had collected, but that only gave the appearance of work. In each chapter I blocked out there were a score or more essential questions that had to be answered before any of the other material could make any sense or have any veracity. We had known this at the time and it had been agreed that after I blocked out the book, the impostor would be available to supply the missing links. When I was through, I had a list of some two hundred vital questions and an equal number of less vital ones—each of them neatly notated on the top of an empty page in a collection of notebooks—waiting for answers I knew were never going to come.

I had one other onerous duty that remained to be done. Sooner or later I was going to have to inform the people at Random House that not only were they not going to get a book about the Great Impostor, as written in their contracts, but that the several thousands of dollars they had advanced to Demara and me was not going to be coming either. Perhaps in the next ten years I would be able to pay it back, like an indentured servant. I would have to become Master Ridley once more to handle this one.

A final irony that disturbed me no end was that when the baby finally came Dr. Monroe could not be present because of an emergency, and our newest girl, Jennifer, was delivered by a young doctor Judy had never set eyes upon until five minutes before the birth. Oh, if only Dr. Demara, hero of Korean waters, had somehow been along to bring a new life into the world and into his own!

Then one drab day in April he called.

"I think I was overdoing this," he said. "And after all, a promise is a promise. All right, ask me a question."

I think the impostor had felt as guilty about those unanswered questions as I had about deceiving him about the birth of the baby. For a renowned and monumental liar, the impostor is notoriously a man of his word, a fact that never fails to confuse, please and astonish me.

We got together all of the next week. It was long, hard, detailed, cruel work, but he never complained. He wanted to get the work done and he was loyal to his promise. But there was something gone between us now. I knew that. Things could never again be the same. We were pleasant, courteous and even funny about incidents but, as far as he was concerned, I had failed him. He had asked for trust, and I didn't trust him. I had been forced, finally, to face up to him and, once having done that, I never stood in the same ambivalent awe of the great impostor. I liked him more now, but it wasn't the same.

There came an afternoon when I came to the last page. I was both relieved and sad and I believe he felt the same way.

"You won't believe this, Fred, but that was the last one. There are no more questions."

I suddenly realized just how tired I was. Even if I could have thought of an important question I wouldn't have asked it. I was tired of myself and of Demara and of everything around me.

"Except one," Demara said. It took all of my strength to ask him which one. He gave me a cunning, even wicked smile.

"Why I do what I do," he said, and broke into a roar of laughter.

I spent a blissfully empty weekend doing nothing but talking children's talk with children and then on Monday morning the telephone rang.

"I'm tired of being Fred Demara," he told me. "If you want to say good-by to him, you'd better come down to the Port Authority bus terminal and see the last of him."

I got my raincoat and left. It struck me then that if this was the end, it was a particularly appropriate time for it. April is an impostor's month. It begins with a Fool's Day but more than that, more than any other month of the year, April is nothing and everything. When the wind is low and the sun is out, the breath of early summer is warm all over it. But let the wind come up, and a few clouds cross the face of the sun, and you realize that April

is really March in disguise and winter is still hiding behind the façade. No matter what face April wears, there's
always another month just behind the mask.

At the terminal I found him waiting in line for a bus
that was bound for Chicago and beyond. He was affable
and extremely friendly but I sensed something different
about him. There was a purposeful air about him; he
seemed more confident and happy than he had before. I
had the strong impression that this was a Demara that I
had never really met before.

"I haven't been idle," he told me. He took out his
wallet and patted it. "I've been doing some credential
collecting. In fact," he said lowly, "I'm not me right now."

I looked at his luggage to see if new initials had been
put on, but the old FWD was merely blocked out with
masking tape.

"The moment I bought this ticket, I became someone
else."

The line began filing onto the bus and he took a seat
near a window. I stood out on the loading platform beneath the window but I found it hard to talk. I didn't
know who I was talking to. The engine finally started up
and I was glad. The clouds had covered the sun and I was
beginning to feel cold. I already felt uneasy enough.

I turned to go but the impostor called me back. Over
the roar of the warming engine he began shouting down
to me.

"You were born in Albuquerque, New Mexico, on
January 30, 1925, is that right?"

I nodded that it was.

"And then your family moved East and you lived in New York and then moved to Bronxville. Correct?"

I told him it was. He seemed to be reading from a card or notebook in his lap. "And after that you went on to that Benedictine school in Rhode Island and after that Harvard?"

It was all in order. The bus began rolling ahead, slowly, and I was standing there waving good-by to the impostor when I realized what was happening to me.

"Wait!" I cried, and started running alongside the bus trying to keep up with it.

"Fred!" He wouldn't turn to look at me then.

The big bus slid out into the heavy traffic on Ninth Avenue and that slowed it enough so that by running hard I was able for a short time to stay alongside it.

"You're me, is that it?" I shouted. "You're me now, aren't you?"

He didn't make a sign or say a word.

I had no malice about it; I had no feeling at all beyond that of wondering what this man in the guise of me might be doing in the world. A few days before I had read him some lines from Dylan Thomas that had moved me and which he told me he wished he had known before his own father had died.

> *Do not go gentle into that good night,*
> *Old age should burn and rave at close of day;*
> *Rage, rage against the dying of the light.*

He could have my name, he was welcome to my past, just let him do something with it that was bright with life. The light had changed and the bus began to roll again.

"Don't go gentle, Fred!" I shouted to him. "I don't care, Fred. Just don't go gentle."

He merely sat up there in the bus, smiling quietly, wearing a look I had never seen him wear before, one finger held over his lips.

I wonder if he ever heard me.

ABOUT THE AUTHOR

ROBERT CRICHTON was born thirty-six years ago in Albuquerque, New Mexico. He attended Portsmouth Priory, a Benedictine school in Rhode Island. From the Priory, he entered the infantry during World War II as a rifleman. He is the son of the late Kyle Crichton and is married to Judy Feiner; they have four children.

Mr. Crichton's first book, *The Great Impostor,* was a bestseller and has been made into a movie. He is now at work on several projects including a novel.